CRIME
IN
PROGRESS

THOMAS FINNERAN

ISBN: 978-1-5356-1504-4

Contents

CHAPTER 1

IT WAS MARCH 1967 WHEN I mustered out of the army after serving a year in Vietnam. I finished up my tour of duty giving small arms training at Fort Jackson, South Carolina. I remember the closer I got to going back to the States the more nervous I got. Men would walk around all day saying, "I'm short," meaning they had begun counting the days until they were airlifted back home. We all felt our luck could run out at any time.

Our family believed in getting good, steady-paying civil service jobs because of the security. My parents had come through tough times and they pushed me in the direction of working for the government. There were only three roads out of our neighborhood: cop, fireman, or Rikers Island inmate. Whenever one of our neighbors got arrested, my father would say, "There but for the grace of God go I." The old man always seemed to aim his comments at me and the lesson wasn't lost on me.

Three years before getting drafted I had taken the cops test in some high school in Queens, New York, and on subsequent passes, before shipping off to Nam, I had taken the medical and physical exams. After an extensive background check, I was certified, and then they wait-listed me until I was discharged. It was the culmination of a lifelong dream. People should be careful what they wish for—they just might get it.

Two months after my discharge I married my high school sweetheart, Karen McEvady, at Good Shepherd Parish in Queens. Our honeymoon at Niagara Falls lasted only a week because I was entering the New York Police Academy the following Monday morning. I suppose that's where my story begins.

After the graduation ceremony we received our assignments, and that meant the 11th Precinct for me. Nobody seemed to know anything good or bad about it, so I asked the training sergeant at the academy if he had any information.

"Yeah. Sure. That's down on the Lower East Side of Manhattan and is a real mix of nationalities.

It's a shithouse, but you'll learn the job fast if it don't kill you first." He laughed. "Good luck, Halley," he said as he shook my hand.

"Thanks, Sarge," I said.

My first day I drew Avenue C and 5th Street, and when I arrived I was welcomed by someone who tried to cave my head in with a radiator thrown from a roof. I chased them up on the roof, but they disappeared like smoke. I remember coming down the stairs and hearing the laughter from the residents and Spanish references to my manhood. It was a lesson of frustration that would be repeated often during my career. It would be a while before I learned how to run down rooftop snipers, thanks in large part to a rugged Italian cop named John Anselmo. He was born and raised on Mott Street in Manhattan, and he didn't take crap from anybody. Anselmo was a Korean War vet who had received the Silver Star for gallantry, and he was an old-school cop who didn't always go by the book

"This is no game out here, Mike!" Anselmo said. "Sometimes the cop on the beat is the only thing standing between some skell and his freedom. Make no mistake, they won't hesitate to take you out."

"It's obvious these people hate us down here, John. How do you put up with it?" I asked.

"Most people want to do the right thing, but they are afraid of reprisals," Anselmo said. "Just remember, Mike, you are now a member of a very well-armed gang that will not tolerate anyone laying hands on you," Anselmo said. "Whenever one of us is getting his ass kicked, somebody is calling the ten-thirteen for assist patrolman. So, they do care."

One trick he showed me was how to survey my post before even stepping foot on it. On a rainy Saturday afternoon, we both climbed the stairs to PS 13 on Avenue D, which was the tallest building in the sector.

"Do you see those adjoining rooftops and the red numbers on those doors?" Anselmo asked. "Yeah, what about it?" I asked.

"Those numbers are code for building numbers on my post That way I know exactly which roof the snipers are working today," Anselmo said.

"Look! There's two scumbags now!" I said, pointing to a rooftop.

"Is that a clothesline they are stringing up?" I asked.

"No, a booby trap," Anselmo said. "They tie wire across the roof that is taller than they are and they hope you're a big-ass cop so you'll cut your head off chasing after them. They are on roof 12, which means 315 E. 5th Street. As soon as it gets dark we'll try to snipe the snipers."

I met John on the corner of 5th and C at about eight o'clock and we headed around by the buildings, staying close to the building line.

"Do you think they are still there?" I asked.

"Yeah. They are waiting for you to walk up this block," Anselmo said. "I have padlocked all the doors on the adjoining rooftops from the inside, so they can't get away from us. Give me five minutes, then follow me up."

I nodded my okay.

Arriving on the top floor, I saw John listening at the door.

"They are on the right side of this door. Can you hear them?" Anselmo said.

I put my ear to the door and could hear their voices as plain as day.

"Here, little piggy, come out, come out wherever you are," the first perp said in broken English.

"Come get your fookin haircut," Perp 2 said, laughing.

"Remember, keep your head down so you don't garrote yourself on those wires, " Anselmo said.

They were both laughing when we broke through the roof door and rushed them.

3

"Oh, SHIT!" they screamed in unison as they took off in their felony flyers across to the next roof. They slid across the soft tar and grabbed the door handle, but the door wouldn't open.

"Fuck," the first perp yelled.

The two perps kept leapfrogging until they reached the last roof and went onto the fire escape, with Anselmo right behind them. I grabbed hold of the edge of the roof and dropped down heavily onto the last roof. Grabbing my ankle, I cursed under my breath for being such a klutz.

"You lousy bastard," Anselmo yelled.

I got up and began running to the edge of the roof when I heard screams from the fire escape. My blood froze, thinking I was too late to save John.

"John! Are you all right?" I yelled.

Reaching the edge of the roof, I looked down and saw the two perps lying in a twisted tangle of limbs, awash in dark black blood.

"What happened, John?" I asked.

"Irony," Anselmo said. "Go down the stairs and call for an ambulance, and for the sergeant on patrol to respond to the alley. After you're done, meet me by the bodies."

"Right away, John," I said.

CHAPTER 2

WE WERE ASKED THE SAME questions over and over again by the duty captain, Internal Affairs sergeant, and our own 11ᵗʰ Detective Squad. Even the assistant DA piped in with her own slant on the scene.

"The DA's office is worried about charges of a cover-up and a possible mini riot down here."

"What is your take on this, Captain?" ADA Kern asked.

"There was no shooting involved, and these low-lifes were known and hated in the community, so there will be no tears shed for them," Captain Shemack said.

"What about the Progressive Labor Organization? Will they start an uproar?" Kern asked.

"Community support isn't there, so they will probably make a protest through some liberal rag like the *Village Voice*," Captain Shermack said. "You can tell the DA this won't affect his election."

"Hey, Cap, are you done with these men, because we need to get started on this paperwork," said Detective Sikorsky.

"They are all yours, Detective," the captain said.

Sikorsky and the other detectives seemed to have stepped right out of central casting because they were everything I had pictured cops to look like. They were big, wisecracking, and rugged-looking individuals who had the look of people who had seen it all. They wore fedoras and rumpled suits, and they all typed with one finger at fifty words a minute.

"Hey, kid, get yourself some coffee while I take your partner's statement," Detective Sikorsky said. "We'll call you when we need you."

Over the years I discovered being called "kid" was the squad's way of pointing out a rookie from a veteran, and it had nothing to do with your age. They called you by name after you earned their respect as a "stand-up cop" and not before.

It was well after 3:00 a.m. when John and I got done and we stopped in at Al Fiore's bar on the corner of 7th and 2nd Avenue. The bar was below street level and was like stepping back in time to the Roaring Twenties where it was used as a speakeasy. Al Fiore was in his seventies and looked like he could still bounce you on your keister.

"Al, this is Mike Halley, a stand-up guy," Anselmo said.

"How the hell are you, Mike?" Al said, shaking my hand. "What's your poison?"

"Anything on tap." I said. "I expect to see Jimmy Cagney pop out of the back room singing 'Yankee Doodle Dandy.'"

"Yeah. HA! Ha! If this place could talk, it would be a bestseller," John said. "Back in the twenties and thirties this place was frequented by the top hoods and cops alike. Oney Madden and Legs Diamond sat at this same bar."

"Al has pictures of a police picnic up in Westchester and they are seen with the police commissioner, Barney Sullivan," John said. "I think that's why Al could do no wrong in the years that followed. He knows where all the bodies are buried."

"What about today? Who frequents it today?" I asked.

"Neighborhood holdouts, both Jewish and Italian families who live in rent-controlled apartments and can't afford to move. Some just love the neighborhood, and others won't be forced out by the Puerto Rican immigrants," John said.

"You mean the way they forced people out when their families moved in fifty years ago?" I asked.

"Exactly!" John laughed at the irony. "It's just history repeating itself."

"I enjoy talking to people who have lived a long time. They know so much history and have so many stories," I said.

"Al tells great stories, but if a guy was an asshole when he was thirty, he will still be an asshole at seventy," John said. "Not that Al is an ass, but some of these old guys have been known to stretch the truth."

"You sure have turned into a cynic in your young age," I said.

"Comes with the job. When you're faced with this human garbage all day long, you'll become like all the rest of us former idealists. You better hope cynic is the worst you become," John said.

"Speaking of the job, what happened on that fire escape?" I asked.

"You read the unusual and the deposition, didn't you?" John answered.

"I just thought there might be more," I said.

"One of the bastards tried to throw me off the damn thing, so I picked him up and threw him into his friend who was hanging from the escape ladder," John said. "Not exactly the way I told it, but now everybody is happy. Except, of course, the two dead skells."

"What's the difference?" I asked.

"One is accidental homicide and the other is at least manslaughter," John said. "Mike, you gotta learn the law inside out if you want to keep from getting jammed up in this job."

"How could what you did tonight get you jammed up?" I asked.

"The grand jury might find no true bill against me for a crime, but lawyers for the skell's family would sue for a wrongful death. They would sue the city, the department, and me personally, and I am not about to make the shitheads who raised these two pieces of garbage rich," John said.

"I never looked at it that way before," I said.

"We have a saying down here that should be gospel for all cops. Better to be tried by twelve than carried by six," John said. "Worry about the safety of you, your partner, and innocent people first, then worry about legalities."

That night I received an education they never taught me in school. John Anselmo's advice would serve me well on many occasions in the years to come.

CHAPTER 3

IT WAS THREE MONTHS LATER before I ran into Anselmo again. While assigned to sector Charlie, a call went out over the radio—"Ten-thirteen assist patrolman at Avenue C and 7th Street."

"Sector Charlie enroute Central."

"Ten-four, Charlie. Who is backing up?" Central asked.

"Sector Eddie."

"Sector King."

"Put the lights and siren on, Mike, this is one time we wanna let them know we're coming," said JC.

A large crowd had gathered in the street but began to disperse when we pulled up.

"Move it! Open up! Let us in!" I ordered.

There, lying on the curb holding his chest, was John Anselmo.

"Oh! My God, John, what happened?" I asked, "Is there an ambulance on the way?" I yelled.

"It's pulling up now," said JC.

John kept mumbling something, but his words had no meaning to me. The Emergency Medical Technicians rushed the gurney through the crowd and into the rear of the ambulance.

"Who will accompany the officer in the wagon?" EMT one asked.

"Who has the sector?" Sergeant. Boyle asked.

"We do, boss. Sector Charlie," JC said.

"Halley, you ride in the bus and Colby can follow in the radio car," Boyle said.

"Okay, Sarge," I said.

"I'll need an aided card, a UF #61, and property vouchers to safeguard his personal property."

Boyle said, "See you at the hospital after I make all the notifications and clear the streets."

As the ambulance headed for Bellevue Hospital, I watched the technician trying to stop the blood and take John's blood pressure.

"Are you getting a pulse?" I asked.

"Very faint," the tech said.

He picked up his radio and called Bellevue.

"EMS #16 to base. Do you read?" the tech asked.

"We read EMS. What is your situation?" Base said.

"Bringing in MOF [Member of Force) with a bullet wound to upper torso, BP one hundred over sixty, saline drip in place, blood flow unremitting. Have crash team stand by for our ETA in three," the tech said.

"Ten-four, we are standing by, sixteen," said the hospital dispatcher.

A few minutes later John was out of the ambulance and in the operating room. Cops brought all gunshot victims to Bellevue and all heart attacks to LI Jewish. The sheer volume of patients at Bellevue with gunshot wounds made their staff experts in their handling these cases. LI Jewish and Maimonides hospitals in Brooklyn were the hospitals with heart research teams that were far ahead in their fields. Your chance of recovery was greatly increased by what hospital worked on you.

They had been working on John for an hour and a half and he was still fighting for his life. All the department brass was there, including the mayor. While I watched the cops waiting to give blood, I saw the department chaplain walking in with a woman, holding her arm while she stared with vacant eyes. "That's got to be John's wife," I said.

"Yeah, I seen her with him at a precinct dance once," said JC.

Seeing Mrs. Anselmo reminded me of a saying I had heard the company commander in Nam say once. "You also serve who stand and wait," I said.

Sergeant Boyle showed up and asked to see the paperwork. He took it from us and said, "Go back to command. There is a twenty-two-job backlog and other precincts are trying to cover for us."

"Right away, boss," JC said. "Keep us informed."

"I will," Boyle said.

It was my turn to drive and JC to be the recorder. The recorder gets stuck with any reports or arrests that we catch for the rest of the tour.

"Let's have the keys, JC. It's time for me to put you in harm's way," I said.

"You know you'll get lost down there, " JC said. "Why don't you let me drive?"

"No good, slick. Hand them over," I said.

"Twenty-two job backlog. Shit. I'll be writing for days," JC whined. "Just don't drive me into a collar tonight. I get to see my kid tomorrow and I can't miss that, " JC said.

Jim Colby, JC, was a twelve-year veteran of the force who had been a detective in narcotics in the Bronx when he got jammed up. He had given his snitches nickel bags of heroin for information and the Internal Affairs Department had caught him. He was busted back into the bag (uniform) and received a thirty-day rip (loss of pay or vacation).

"How come they never locked you up? Isn't giving drugs to people considered sale?" I asked.

"My life and career are over. Isn't that enough?" JC said.

It took over two hours of non-stop response to clear up the backlog. It was ten-thirty before we were allowed to go to meal. I drove down by the water near the ballfields on FDR Drive. While JC tried to catch up on his memo book entries, I stared out at the East River and wondered how Anselmo was doing. I tried to figure out who could have done it, and why. What the hell was he trying to say to me back on the street? "Ten-thirty by the mop," John had said. Ravings of a guy going into shock, I surmised.

John Anselmo died from his wounds three days after the shooting and received an inspector's funeral. Over four thousand men in blue from all over the country were at his wake and burial at St. John's Cemetery in Queens. For the first time as an adult I openly wept.

I made a promise to myself that I would try to keep tabs on the case so John wouldn't be forgotten, and to keep bugging the squad about where they were at from time to time.

"You know, Mike, we are invited to my mother's for dinner tonight. Or did you forget?" Karen asked.

"No, honey, I didn't forget," I said. "I love your mom's cooking."

"Since you went on that job you seem to be a million miles away," Karen said.

"Oh, I'm sorry if I've been aloof lately. I'm still trying to get my bearings," I said.

"Our neighbor, Craig Higgins, is a cop and he is off with his family a lot," Karen said.

"Higgins is a clerical man in headquarters who works banker's hours. They should give him hazardous duty pay for paper cuts," I said.

"There! That's what I'm talking about. You never used to be so critical of others, and now you have something nasty to say about everyone," Karen said.

"Oh, honey, come here and tell me what's wrong with you. Did you have an argument with your mom today?" I asked.

"No, Michael, I did not have an argument with anybody. Not yet anyway, " Karen said. The ominous threat in her voice, and the fact that she called me Michael, told me that she wasn't kidding. I put my arms around her and asked her what was wrong.

"I have some news I have been trying to tell you, but you seem oblivious to everything," Karen said.

"What news?" I asked.

"We are going to have a baby, that's what news!" Karen purred.

Getting hit with a sledgehammer would have had less impact than Karen's news. Standing there like a Venus flytrap, mouth open, eyes beginning to glaze over, I tried to speak.

"Er. Aaahh. Really! Oh my God, that's great, honey. I'm so happy. When did you find out? Does your mother know?" I mumbled.

"You're the first to hear the news. Are you sure you're happy?" Karen asked.

"Are you kidding? This is the greatest news I could have heard," I said. "Let's celebrate."

That night we went out to O'Leary's Steak House in Sunnyside, Queens. I had a little too much Irish coffee, but Karen didn't seem to mind.

"Having a child is a life-altering event, Mike," Karen said. "Once this baby is born you will have to show more responsibility about your actions," Karen said while pointing to my glass.

"I will, Karen. I promise I'll be the best parent you ever saw," I said.

That night was one of the happiest of my life, second, of course, to the birth of my daughter

Annie Lynne Halley nine months later. Yes, life was good, and God was in his heaven.

CHAPTER 4

IT WAS ALMOST TEN MONTHS later, and the squad seemed to be dead in the water on the John Anselmo murder.

"What's going on, Sikorsky? Anything new?" I asked.

"No, Mike, nothing yet, but we are still actively pushing all the right buttons and we put the word out on the street that we have over ten thousand in reward money. Cases on cop killers are never closed," Sikorsky said.

"Got any new leads?" I asked.

"Yeah, but this guy has had too much 'Sneaky Pete' to be a credible witness," Sikorsky said.

"What do you mean?" I asked.

"Some wino from the men's shelter at 8 East 3rd Street said he saw a guy arguing with Anselmo before the shooting, but we couldn't verify his story," Sikorsky said.

"Did he give you a description?" I asked.

"Yeah. A tall, dark Caucasian. Maybe a mob guy is the way he put it. So we didn't put much faith in what he saw," Sikorsky said. "But something will break soon, I'm sure."

"What was wino's name?" I asked.

"Roy Rogers. Really. We checked it from his veteran's check-cashing card. That's some moniker to be stuck with, huh, Mike," Sikorsky said.

"Maybe the death of his horse Trigger is what made him a drunk," I said.

"Ha. Ha. That's a good one, kid," Sikorsky sneered. "Now, take a hike! I have detecting to do."

After leaving the squad, I headed to the muster room and began taking the stolen car alarms for that night. A new directive had come down giving any officer who made two arrests for grand larceny auto within six months an Excellent Police Duty commendation and two days off, per collar. Time off from this circus was essential if you wanted to keep your sanity.

"Trying for more days off, Halley?" Phil Oliveri teased.

"Anytime out of this asylum is life affirming," I said.

I didn't like Oliveri much, or his partner Dave Walden for that matter. They had Sector King, the best sector in the precinct, and I thought they were a couple crooks with badges. Oliveri scared me a little, too. He was over sixty-two inches and weighed in at a muscular two hundred and thirty pounds. He had dark features with a boxers pushed-in nose that he received while practicing some new form of fighting called tae kwon do, an Asian form of self-defense. He had practiced every day since the age of eleven and had attained the fourth-degree black belt. The stories about his fighting ability were legendary in the department and he didn't seem to mind throwing his weight around. His partner Walden was a nervous kind of guy with a big mouth. A sleazebag that needed Oliveri to keep him from getting his jaw broke. All in all, two guys to stay away from.

"Hey, Halley! Weren't you in Viet Nam?" Oliveri asked.

"That's right. Why?" I asked.

Opening his uniform shirt, he showed me a T-shirt that had a picture of Jane Fonda with the words "Frag Jane Fonda" under the picture.

"What do you think?" he asked.

"Words to live by," I said. "She should have been tried for treason for giving aid and comfort to the enemy during wartime."

"She is a wrong-minded liberal that should have been held accountable for her actions," I said. "Her actions, and the actions of others of her ilk, helped prolong the war and strengthened the resolve of the NVA to fight on. We wasted lives of American servicemen in a war we had no stomach for," I said.

The men in the room began clapping and marching while humming "America the Beautiful." "Bravo! Bravo!" JC said.

"Don't sugarcoat it, Halley, tell us what you really feel," laughed Sergeant Boyle.

"Having rage like that inside you can make you sick," said Oliveri.

"FALL IN," ordered Sergeant Boyle.

Cops try to see the humor in everything. Otherwise, the stress of dealing with tragedies on a daily basis would drive most of us to the psycho ward at Bellevue.

We had just started making a run through our sector when we came across a small crowd on the corner of 5th and Avenue A. A bystander flagged us down and said, "There is somebody bad hurt over there. You'll see, you'll see. Hurry. "

On the ground lay a young Spanish boy, about sixteen, being cradled by another older Spanish male.

"What happened here?" I asked. "Who are you?"

"This is my brother Frankie Rodriguez. We were just sparring around, man, when I hit him and he fell hard to the ground. I didn't mean to hurt him," said Juan Rodriguez.

There was a lump over the right eye of the unconscious boy, and his movements suddenly became jerky and his body went completely taut.

"JC, give the ambulance a second call, and get an ETA," I said. "How do you feel, Frankie? Can you see me?" I asked.

Some gurgling sounds came from his throat, and suddenly his body lurched backward, and his eyes rolled back in his head until only the whites showed. He was gagging, and I was afraid he was going to swallow his tongue or lacerate it while in this seizure.

"What's happening? Madre mia. Help him," Juan pleaded.

I jammed the leather cover of my memo book into his mouth.

"Your brother is having a seizure and I wanna make sure he doesn't hurt himself," I said.

The violent spasms continued getting worse, even after he was loaded into the ambulance. The attendant got him tied to the gurney and he seemed to quiet down a bit.

Later that night the detectives arrested Juan Rodriguez and charged him with reckless endangerment and manslaughter, as his brother Frankie never regained consciousness. Apparently, the punch caused a massive blood clot to the brain.

"I feel sorry for Rodriguez and his family," I said.

"They should know better at their age than to be punching one another in the head," said JC. "That machismo bullshit always ends up bad."

"You might be right, but still, it's a hell of a thing to live with the rest of his life," I said.

"Fuck 'em all," JC said.

"Do you need the Raid, JC?" I asked.

"Raid! What for?" JC asked.

"For that bug up your ass!" I said.

We both started to laugh and couldn't stop for some time. The tension he was feeling seemed to have broken with the laughter.

"Seriously, JC, what's going on with you? You've had a case of the ass for days now," I asked.

"My wife and her new husband are moving to Seattle, Washington. My son will be over three thousand miles away from me. Can you believe that shit, Mike?" JC said.

"Really! What did your lawyer say?" I asked.

"I'm broke, Mike. I can't afford any more legal fees," JC said.

"You can't let them go without a fight," I said. "I'll loan you the money. I still have my mustering-out pay," I said.

"I can't borrow from you, Mike. I don't know when I could pay you back," JC said.

"You need to move on this right away, to get a court order stopping them before they disappear," I said. "Don't worry about the money, just worry about your son." I wrote out a check for eight hundred dollars and gave it to JC before the end of our tour.

He called his lawyer's service and told them he would be in bright and early the next morning. They tried to put him off, but he told the service it was an emergency and he needed a court order preventing his wife from leaving the state with his son.

"They want me in before half past eight because my attorney has to be in court tomorrow," JC said. "So, I'll be staying in the crib tonight at the station house."

"That's good because I have to be at criminal court tomorrow myself," I said. "That burglary case on Houston Street and Avenue B."

"The one where the idiot got stuck in the duct system?" JC asked.

"Yeah," I laughed. "That's the one. He'll probably use the stupidity defense."

"Do you remember him saying that he thought if he got his head through the opening, then the rest of him could squeeze through easy?" JC asked.

"I hope his lawyer doesn't put this genius on the stand, because the jury might hurt themselves laughing at his testimony," I said while laughing hysterically.

"Yeah, that should be fun to watch," JC said. "Listen, Mike, thanks again for the loan. I really appreciate it. I'll give it back as soon as I can."

"Don't mention it, JC, and good luck tomorrow," I said.

I watched him head up the stairs to the top floor bunk area and felt kind of sorry for him. His career and his personal life were in the crapper and he was struggling to hold on to the only person who cared about him, his son. I just hoped that Karen saw it the same way when I told her about the loan.

In the morning, after I shaved and showered, I went to the muster room on the ground floor. The day tour was a mob scene. Everybody was going to criminal court, or traffic court, or worse, to Internal Affairs down on Poplar Street in Brooklyn. Another investigation was being conducted at the 11th Precinct and still nobody knew what it was about or who was involved. Forty-two post changes to court were read at roll call, while the regular platoon moaned about getting some coffee.

"Settle down, ladies," Sergeant Kenny said. "We'll be done here soon."

"See the crap you have to put up with when you're active, Sarge?" asked Neil Rienhart.

"If you don't pick up your arrest activity, Reinhart, you'll be walking a post on the Bowery," said Sergeant Kenny.

"Ooohh! Aaahh!" The room reverberated with catcalls.

"Take your post!" ordered Sergeant Kenny.

I went to Tattner's for breakfast. Oliveri was already at a table when I walked in and he was breaking the waiter's onions.

"I'll take bacon and two eggs over light with home fries," Oliveri said.

"I'm sorry, Officer, but we are a kosher restaurant and don't serve bacon," said Bruce.

"Oh. Okay. Just the eggs and potatoes then," Oliveri said. As the waiter was walking away from the table, Oliveri started to laugh out loud and said, "They don't like pig meat! I keep forgetting that."

The other cops smiled out of fear, I assumed. I was embarrassed by his actions.

"Don't let that idiot get to you, Bruce," I said to the waiter as he was passing by.

"That putz comes in here every week and asks for the same order and I tell him the same thing all the time," Bruce said. "Kind of sad, don't you think, Mike?"

"You don't know the half of it," I said.

"That big one, Oliveri, he is just like a whitewashed tomb. Beautiful on the outside, but his insides are full of dead men's bones," Bruce said.

As Bruce walked away, shaking his head, I was struck by his words and his assessment of the cop. I decided that Bruce was the best judge of people I had ever met and should be teaching philosophy instead of putting up with the likes of Oliveri.

CHAPTER 5

ENTERING THE TRIAL PART OF the Criminal Courts Building was like trying to find your train at Grand Central Station. Mass confusion reigned supreme. The hallways were clogged with lawyers and their clients, and their assorted entourages of friends and relatives.

After finding the room number of my trial part, I checked the docket printed on the wall. Scanning the names of the cases, I saw that my case, Mendez, was number eight out of eighty-eight scheduled. With such an early call I might get to go home early today, I thought. I entered the courtroom and sat in a bench near the prosecutor's table.

"All rise! Supreme Court Part 11 is now in session. The Honorable Justice David Goldman presiding. Put away all newspapers, books, and magazines. Stop all talking. Attorneys having cases on the docket today approach and be heard," the court clerk said. "Docket #801789, case of Walsh, on a charge of armed robbery in the second degree," the clerk said.

"Warren Castillo for the defense, Your Honor."

"Are you ready for trial, Mr. Castillo?" Judge Goldman asked.

"We are, Your Honor," Castillo said.

"Mark it ready for trial, room 112 this morning," Goldman said. "Next case."

The court clerk began calling other docket numbers, but many didn't answer and were marked for a second call. The clerk seemed to be calling all the cases where there was private representation. My guy couldn't afford his own attorney, so that meant we wouldn't get called until all the other attorneys were done.

Judge Goldman was moving along real fast and he was now getting to cases where the defendants were being kept in holding pens. They were brought out by court officers in cuffs and stood before the bench.

"Docket #811842, case of Mendez, arresting officer Halley from the 11th," the clerk said. "The charge is burglary second degree."

I approached the table in front of the bench and nodded to the Bridgeman that I was present. Mendez was brought out by a court officer in cuffs.

"Who's your lawyer?" the court clerk asked Mendez.

Mendez turned to his left and right and shrugged his shoulders. "I'm not sure," Mendez said.

"What's your lawyer's name?" the clerk asked.

"Er. Aaahhh. Daly, I think," said Mendez.

"Michael Daly?" the clerk asked.

"Yes! That's the name," Mendez said.

"Michael Daly is the prosecutor in your case, Mr. Mendez," the clerk said.

"I don't know then," Mendez said.

"Legal aid, Mr. Munson, is Mendez one of your cases?" the clerk asked.

Fumbling through a huge bundle of file folders, Bob Munson found the file on Mendez and saw a notation on the side of the folder that read "ready for trial."

"I'm sorry, Your Honor, for the delay," Munson said while trying to show the judge how large his case load was by lifting the folders up in the air. "We are ready to proceed, Your Honor."

"Mark it ready, room 112, Judge Isaacs," Judge Goldman said.

As I entered room 112, I saw Jonas Mandel seated in the outer witness room and I greeted him and asked, "What are you doing here?"

"I got a summons to appear today. Do you think I will have to testify?" Mandel asked. "I'm very nervous."

"Have you talked to ADA Daly yet?" I asked.

"No. I haven't talked to anyone about this case," Mandel said.

"Usually they just take your sworn deposition if you aren't a witness or have something tangible to offer in the case, other than being the owner of the property and not giving him permission to be there," I said. "Take a seat and I'll see if the ADA needs us both."

Approaching Daly, I told him that the owner of the building on the Mendez case was outside and

I wondered if he was needed for trial.

After looking through his case file he began shaking his head and said, "How the heck did he get a summons to appear? We don't need him, Officer. Send him home with our thanks," Daly said.

Mandel was greatly relieved when I told him he could go home and asked me to let him know the outcome of the case.

I watched Munson and Daly talking on the side of the courtroom when I walked back in and sat down.

"May we approach, Your Honor?" Daly asked.

Motioning them to come forward, Judge Isaacs put his hand over the microphone and listened to Daly speak. They went back to their respective places and Munson said, "Your Honor, the defense wishes to change our not guilty plea to guilty of burglary third degree."

"Does the prosecution have any objections?" Judge Isaacs asked.

"That's acceptable, Your Honor," Daly said.

"Sentencing date April 12th, my court," Judge Isaacs said.

Just like that the case was over and I was heading back to the police sign-in room for my court slip, and then back to the 11th.

Mendez would get another line on his yellow sheet and do a few years in Rikers Island. The justice system seemed so impersonal. Legal aid attorneys overworked and underpaid, against a well-armed prosecutor's office with plenty of money and manpower to get the job done. All the actors in this drama were nameless faces, moving from one room to another, without one iota of human compassion being shown by anyone.

This was the fifteenth felony arrest I had made and the names and faces of those men were already a blur to me. I hoped and prayed that I would not become so callous as to forget that there was still a human side to doing this job.

It was noon by the time I reported to the 11th Precinct from court.

"Halley, back from court. No meal, Sarge," I said to the desk officer.

"You're supposed to salute when you speak to a desk officer, Halley," Sergeant Cosoff said.

Standing in front of the desk, I saluted and repeated my earlier statement. "PO Halley back from court, no meal," I said, holding the salute.

"At ease, Halley," Cosoff said. "What post did you have when you turned out?" Cosoff asked.

"The Bowery," I said.

"Take a one o'clock meal and stick with that post. The vets are getting their checks today so watch them young junkies who will be waiting for them to cash out," Cosoff said.

Sergeant Cosoff was a typical spit and polish boss who had never seen any action in the service, or on the job. Ordering everybody around on minor regulations was his way of showing how much of a man he was. In Nam, the men who were the loudest were the most afraid. "That son of a bitch has some nerve shooting his mouth off about saluting and petty crap like that. He is the biggest goniff I ever saw," whispered Paul Abrams, who was working the switchboard. "He is an embarrassment to my nationality."

Paul was the "Shorim" society delegate and he and Cosoff were both members of the police department Jewish fraternal order. The word goniff is Yiddish for thief, and Cosoff had a reputation for taking anything not nailed down.

"Don't let it bother you, Paul. His kind always gets his in the end," I said. I gave Paul a meal location and a telephone number where I could be reached and headed to post.

CHAPTER 6

AFTER EATING A COUPLE OF Nathan's franks for lunch, I took a slow stroll along my post, which covered 1st to 4th Street, from 2nd Avenue to the Bowery. It was a little after 2:00 p.m. when I noticed two young junkies duck quickly into an alley off 2nd Street. Trotting to the edge of the alley, I glanced down its length while hiding the rest of me behind the building. The two vultures had grabbed an old bum and had pushed him up against a wall where they were cutting his pockets open with a knife.

"You lousy, thieving bastards," yelled the bum.

"Shut up, pops, and maybe I won't cut your throat," said the perp with the knife.

I was on top of the two robbers before they knew what happened and smacked the armed perp in the side of the head with my slapper (flat iron in leather).

"Owww!" screamed the perp as he dropped to the pavement, holding his head.

"Don't hurt me, Officer, I didn't mean nothing by it," said the second perp as he backed up against the alley wall.

"Get down on the ground," I said to the second perp.

I cuffed the uninjured one behind his back and had an aide from the men's shelter call for a sector car for arrest transportation, and an ambulance for the knife wielder.

The old guy had fallen to the sidewalk during the apprehension and had an ugly-looking gash over his right eye that would need stitches to close. He had the typical look of a Bowery resident, that is, a blank expression on his face and the sunken, lifeless eyes that were slow to keep up with his head movements.

"Are you okay, old-timer?" I asked.

He looked straight at me and seemed to be weighing the question when he said, "Yes, but they got my army fatigue jacket and my veterans money."

The perp with the jacket on was the one I'D jacked, and when I rolled him over to take the victim's jacket off him, there was a small .25 caliber automatic handgun lying underneath him.

"What's this?" I exclaimed. "I think I took you too lightly." I didn't search and cuff the perp right away, and that mistake could have cost me my life. "We'll just see if the ballistics on this piece can close some other outstanding cases, you piece of garbage," I said.

There was over two hundred dollars on the inside of the jacket, along with a check-cashing card in the name of Roy Rogers of #8 East 3rd Street.

"Roy Rogers!" I exclaimed.

"Yeah, I heard all the cowboy jokes," Rogers said. "After forty years they ain't funny anymore."

"No, it's not the name that got my attention, but the idea that you might know something about an argument that Police Officer Anselmo had the day he was murdered," I said.

"Who? I don't know about any murder," Rogers said.

"You told Detective Sikorsky you seen him arguing down on Avenue C," I said. "Do you remember?"

"Yesterday is a blur to me and you want me to remember something that happened a thousand bottles ago," Rogers said.

"You're sober now, so how about helping me out. He was my friend," I said.

Rogers stared vacantly at me and seemed to be mulling over the question when he said, "Okay, I'll tell you what I remember, 'cause the cop always treated me with respect, not like a bum." Rogers grabbed my arm and said, "Give me a hand."

After getting to his feet he began to tell his story.

"I was across the street cashing my government check when I see Anselmo arguing with this guy in the street. I thought there was gonna be an arrest cause the cop grabs this guy by the shirt and pushes him against a car. But he doesn't lock him up. Instead he points at him and says something like, 'You been warned,'" Rogers said.

"Then what happened?" I asked.

"The guy gets in his car and leaves. That was it," Rogers said.

"My eye is starting to hurt. Where is that ambulance?" Rogers complained, while holding the handkerchief to the wound.

"The ambulance is on its way. Do you remember anything about the guy or his car?" I asked.

"The man was white, well-dressed for the neighborhood. The car was a white Ford Falcon, I think," Rogers said. "That's all I know, Officer, so now can I have a swig from my bottle?" Rogers asked.

I handed him his bottle of cheap wine and waited for him to drink it down.

"Are you ready to go to the hospital and have your head looked at?" I asked.

"Could you take me to Beth Israel instead of Bellevue?" Rogers asked.

Why? Are you afraid of getting caught in the roundup?" I asked.

"No. It's only fourteen blocks to Beth Israel while Bellevue is over thirty blocks to walk back from," Rogers said.

"Why don't you catch a bus straight down 2nd Avenue?" I asked.

"Bus drivers don't let bums ride. They say we stink up the seats. The subways are too dangerous for me at night, so I have to walk," Rogers said.

I drove back to the station house with the patrol sergeant while the prisoners were taken to the squad room by Sector David. When I got up to the squad room, Detective Andretti asked me if I wanted the collar and I figured I had spent enough time at work, so I gave it to the squad. It was a practice that was done often, and it was probably illegal, but no one seemed to mind. Maybe the defense attorneys might harp on who was actually the arresting officer on the scene, but the detectives were used to testifying and could not be shaken.

Parking was brutal in Jackson Heights due to all the co-ops and illegal multiple family dwellings, but tonight I found a spot after only three trips around the block. When I walked through the front door, Karen was in the kitchen making dinner. "Hello, stranger! How was your day?" Karen asked.

I began to tell her all that had happened, except some of the sordid details. When I told her about the eight hundred dollars I'd loaned JC for his lawyer, I thought she would go through the roof, but all she said was, "If money can help him save his relationship with his son, then it is money well spent."

"You're one of a kind, Mrs. Halley," I said as we hugged in our cramped kitchen.

"My needs are small. A roof over my head, three squares a day, and a million dollars in the bank," Karen said. "That's not much to ask for, is it?"

"The three squares a day might be a problem, but the rest is in the bag," I laughed.

CHAPTER 7

THE NEXT TWELVE MONTHS SEEMED to fly by, what with work and being forced to look for a house. I had planned to start looking for a house in about a year, but Karen had complained that our neighbors in the apartment building did not like children, and she was told to keep her kid out of the garden.

"This old bitty tells me to keep Annie out of the garden or the flowers will never grow!" Karen said. "Can you believe the unmitigated nerve of the woman? The last time a flower grew in that tar pit, Roosevelt was still president," Karen fumed.

"Who was it?" I asked. "Do I know her?"

"You're never here, Michael! I have to see these crones every day and deal with their snide remarks," Karen said. "I want my own place, Michael, where Annie can grow up around people that appreciate life and she can play in her own garden whenever she wants to. Is that too much to ask?"

"No, of course not, honey. We'll start looking this weekend," I said.

I knew better than to argue with Karen when she had her Irish up, so I just let her rant and rave while staying out of her way. I thought we could wait awhile before we started looking for a house, but Karen was right about me not being there. The people in this apartment house were old and settled in their ways. Some of them had even complained to the super of the building about how noisy the children were in the complex. I never told Karen because I knew she would obsess about it and finally blow her top. As far as I knew, we were the only occupants of the building with a young child, so the complaint was directed straight at us.

"Screw the old prunes," Bill Madden said. "I have been the super in this building for over twenty-five years and they forget how nice it is to have the laughter of children. They have grown bitter in their old age."

"Thanks for the heads up, Bill," I said. "I don't know what to say about it except that we'll try to accommodate the neighbors."

Madden hadn't been the super of the building for twenty-five years without being a good politician, so I was sure he had agreed with the old women when they came to him to complain.

It didn't take long before they went directly to the source of their aggravation, Karen and Annie. The gauntlet was thrown, so it was either fight or flight. We chose the latter.

We had been looking for a house in upstate New York for the last few months, but nothing had caught Karen's eye. The houses that were within commuting distance of the city were small and expensive. Houses that fit our budget were over two hours' commute. Of course, when I say these houses fit our budget, I'm talking about me living on bread and water for a few years. We were both getting very depressed looking for the American dream, but whenever we saw our wonderful neighbors sitting out on their lawn chairs, we resolved to try again the following weekend.

Most of the men I worked with in the 11th were commuters from Staten Island or from Long Island. I told Karen that Long Island was less than an hour away and the houses were reasonable.

"You get a lot more house for the money and the schools are excellent," I said. "With the money we save on the house, we can buy a new car for the commuting."

"Just as long as I don't have to put up with those blue-haired backbiters anymore," Karen said while blowing away some of her long, red hair that had gotten into her eyes.

During my lifetime I had noticed that God had created beautiful colors in animals and flowers, but the bright colors in animals were meant as warnings. The coral snake, rock fish, and my wife were colored by God in just such a way.

"You know, I think your red hair kinda glows when you're angry, Karen, " I said.

"Your head will be glowing after I bounce this frying pan off it," Karen said while pointing the pan in my direction.

I feigned fear and ran and picked up Annie and said, "Don't let that bad old monster get us, Annie!"

"Don't you get her in a dither, Michael. She'll be eating soon, and I don't want her stomach upset by a buffoon like you."

"Okay, already. The buffoon has to put you back, Annie. Daddy's sorry."

I went into the living room and clicked on the TV as I sat on the couch. It was back to work tomorrow, and I prayed that we'd find a house before Karen got sick over the stress of living here.

It was early December and the city was already decked out in its Christmas finery, with lights of every color blinking to the sounds of "Jingle Bells," "White Christmas," and Jose Feliciano's "Feliz Navidad" blaring out of every bodega on the East Side.

The weather was particularly cold for this time of year, and wet snow was beginning to fall as I parked my car and walked to the precinct. The windows of the apartments down here didn't have any decorations like they had in Queens, but everyone had a steel gate across the dirty panes of glass. Putting food on the table for some of these people was a tall order and they didn't have money for Christmas decorations. The families with young kids seemed to be particularly depressed this time of the year. You could see the poverty etched in all their faces.

"Attention to roll call!" Sergeant Boyle ordered. As he went down the names on the onion skin paper the cops reply to their names seemed tired and remote.

"Here," said Tomlinson.

"Here," said Williams.

"Okay, men, listen up," said Boyle.

"'Tis the season to be jolly, so that means robberies and burglaries are up, as well as family feuds. Be aware of the stores and businesses in your sectors, and the shoppers, especially on 14th Street. Stop in and say hello to the business people. It makes them feel more secure, and they might be able to point out suspicious people eyeing their stores. Make memo book entries on all visits to stores, as our friends from Internal Affairs are prevalent this time of year. Keep your eyes open and don't become a plaque on the wall of fame. Take your post."

There were seven plaques of hero cops who died in the line of duty in the 11th Precinct hanging behind the desk. They were all recent. The taboos on killing cops seemed to be off since the civil rights protests and all the left-wing radicals. Cops were looked on as lackeys of the military industrial complex and should be attacked as oppressors. All in all, not a very good time to be a cop, or an American for that matter.

"Those bastards!" JC yelled. "They were supposed to make an appointment for this car at the shop today, and they didn't." Car #1120 was smoking and sputtering while idling near the station house.

"I guess as long as the heater works, riding beats walking in this weather," I said.

"Yeah, Luca and Clark would rather commit suicide than walk a beat," JC said. "I'll fix their ass! I'll put the car out of service just before the end of tour, so those two butterballs will have no choice tomorrow but walk. "

"What happens to us then? The car won't be back for a week and that puts us on foot, and then we get to fly to other commands and stand fixed posts all night," I said.

"Don't worry, I 'Il make arrangements with the shop to borrow a car for the 4 to 12 tour only," JC said.

JC looked like he was getting all stressed out over the small stuff again, which prompted me to ask, "How are you making out with your custody battle?"

"Every time we go to court my wife's lawyer keeps asking for a continuance. The judge marked it final for them this Friday. That's when I'll find out if I get to see my kid anymore," JC said.

I wanted to ask him how much it was costing him, but I thought it would sound as if I were more interested in the money than his son, so I avoided the subject like the plague. We had just bought our coffee when the dispatcher called our designation.

"Eleven Charlie. Eleven Charlie, respond."

"Eleven Charlie Central," I said.

"Charlie, see a complainant at 280 East 6th Street."

"What's the job, Central?"

"All he said was there are strange odors coming from an apartment at that location."

"Charlie, read direct, Central," I said.

"Strange smells my ass. This whole precinct has a strange smell to it," JC said.

"Ain't that the truth," I said while laughing into my coffee cup.

Turning into 6th Street, we saw a man waving furiously in the street. Nearing the curb, the complainant stepped to my window and said, "My name is Jorge Torres and I called the police...I'm the super of this building."

"What's the problem, Mr. Torres?" I asked.

"Come. I show you. Come," Torres said while motioning us to follow him.

"I hate this come follow me routine," JC mumbled. "Who the hell knows what we're walking into."

Naturally, the job was on the top floor and JC and I were both winded when we got there.

"This is it," Torres said, pointing to 5C. "It smells bad."

I approached the door and put my face near the doorknob. "Whew," I said, recoiling from the odor. "It's a DOA."

"Are you sure?" asked JC.

"Oh, yeah, I'm sure. Once you've been exposed to the smell of decomposing human flesh, you never forget it," I said.

"Do you have a duplicate key, Mr. Torres?" I asked.

Torres pulled a large key ring from his belt and began trying the lock. The door opened only slightly as it was held in place by a police lock on the inside of the door. "Looks like we'll have to go through the fire escape window, JC," I said.

"Okay. While I'm doing that, you can make the notifications and have the boss eighty-five us with some ammonia. We're gonna need it!" JC said.

After breaking the window on the fire escape, JC entered and removed the steel bar from the rear of the door. As the door opened, the smell rushed out and caught Torres unprepared and he gripped the bannister of the stairs and lurched forward.

"Aahhhh," Torres exhaled as he began to vomit down the entire flight of stairs.

"This is not a good day to be a super, is it, Mr. Torres?" JC teased.

Torres let go again, just missing me as I was returning from the phone call.

"Is that you tossing your cookies, JC?" I asked.

"Yeah, you wish! I'm afraid that Torres got a snootful of the afterlife of apartment 5C."

JC chuckled. We wanted the super to be a witness when we entered the apartment, but he could barely manage standing in the hallway.

"Are you okay out there?" JC grinned as he waited for Torres's reply.

"I'm good, aaahhhh." Torres heaved again in the doorway.

"You're some ball-breaker," I said, pushing JC. "Leave the poor guy alone."

The victim appeared to be a male about sixty or seventy years of age sitting upright in his bathtub, his right arm hanging outside with deep cuts across his wrist. The tub was filled with a dark, foul-smelling liquid, probably a mix of water and body fluids. On the wall, over the tub, was a suicide note.

> *To the Authorities,*
>
>   *Since the death of my wife Bernice, three months ago, I no longer have any interest in living. She was my life for forty-five years and I miss her terribly. I'm sorry for the mess.*
>
> *To my children, David and Bella,*
>
>   *You were always too busy for your Mother and Father in life, so I hope you can find the time to see me in death.*
>
> *Signed, Ira Stem.*

"God! That is a gruesome note to leave your kids," I said.

"They probably deserve it," JC said. "What kind of self-absorbed brats would let their parents stay in a shithole like this?"

"People who commit suicide aren't right in the head, JC," I said. "They are usually looking to punish the living when they kill themselves."

"Is that psychology 101 your spouting?" JC said rhetorically.

"Doesn't this kind of stuff bother you anymore?" I asked.

JC just waved me off and began breaking ammonia capsules in the apartment, trying to mask the odor. We stepped closer to the broken window for some air and waited for the squad.

It took a couple of hours to finish up the paperwork and have a footman sit on the DOA until the medical examiner arrived. Leaving the station, JC turned down East 4th Street and headed back down to our sector. Turning from 4th Street onto Avenue C, we saw a large crowd blocking the street and sidewalks.

"Oh. Oh! What the hell is going on?" JC asked.

"This doesn't look right, JC."

"Watch out!" JC yelled as a Molotov cocktail exploded on the roof of our radio car, sending streams of liquid fire onto the windows and doors.

"Don't stop! Gun the engine," I ordered.

A bottle smashed through the back window and another cocktail struck my window without breaking.

"Ten-thirteen, sector Charlie, Avenue C and 4th Street. Use caution. Molotov cocktails and bottles being thrown by large crowd."

"Ten-thirteen in the 11th Precinct sector, car needs assistance. What units are responding?"

"Sector Adam."

"Sector John, enroute."

"Eleven sergeant responding."

As we drove away quickly, the lighted gas rolled off the car and fell harmlessly into the street. "We look like yellow-bellies to these scumbags for running away!" JC yelled.

"They wanted us to stop so they could have stationary targets to bombard," I said. "We'd be toasted marshmallows by now! They looked like they were waiting for us."

"They just wanted to rob the supermarket and we stumbled on them, that's all," JC said.

"Those Molotov cocktails came from both sides of the street and the rooftops. They were ready for cops, any cops. Count yourself lucky," I said.

As the other units began pulling up to the scene, most of the crowd began filtering away, while the hardcore rabble rousers stood their ground and began chanting.

"No more police brutality! Hell no, we won't go." The crowd roared.

We explained to the boss that we stumbled over the unruly crowd, and that the whole thing seemed to be orchestrated from the get-go. We were relieved around 12:30 a.m. by the TPF (tactical patrol force).

"The TPF will make things worse with all their car stops and bullshit harassment," JC said.

"Maybe the residents will appreciate us more after TPF gets done with them," I said. "Plus, we don't have to put up with petty street crime for a while, since they collar anything with a pulse."

"They will have two cops on every corner for weeks, and when they leave it goes back to just you and me partner. We'll have to undo all the bad feelings they caused," JC said.

"These bastards tried to smoke our asses and you resent them being put through the ringer for what they did!" I said.

"I got a good look at that skell who threw the cocktail at my window, and when things quiet down, I'm gonna find him and jack his ass up and down the block," JC said.

As we drove away from Avenue C that night, I couldn't help but feel sorry for the people who lived down here and how they were being used by left wingers to create unrest in the communities. All the store windows had been broken and fires were still burning in some garbage cans along Avenue C, and it reminded me of the towns in Nam after a battle. I couldn't wait to get the hell out of there and get back across enemy lines.

"Hard to believe that we're the enemy down here," I said. "I thought I'd be helping people."

"Our job is to keep these people from killing each other, and for me and you to go home every night the same way we came to work," JC said. "Everything in between is just bullshit."

CHAPTER 8

My family spent the holidays at my parents' house in upstate New York. Karen's sister and her two screwball brothers were in attendance, along with my father's brother John. Karen's brothers were named Jarod and Slade after some soap actors on TV. They loved to drink beer and tell jokes. Their sister Lara was named after the heroine of the movie *Dr. Zhivago*. Being the older sister, and with her mother's passing, Lara took on the job of raising her brothers for the past ten years.

Earlier in the year, Slade had married a widow with three pre-teenage boys. One of the boys had gotten a baseball glove from Karen, and my uncle John, a semi-pro baseball player in his day, began to tease the boy.

"Can you catch anything with that glove?" John teased.

Looking slightly away, Slade Jr. said, "Sure can."

"What position do you play, Slade?" John asked.

"Pitcher," Slade said proudly.

"A pitcher? Are you any good?" John asked.

With a very serious face the boy looked at my uncle and said, "My coach said I'm very fast."

That was the opening my uncle had elicited from every one of us for the past thirty years.

"Well, then, let's see just how fast you really are," John stated. Off they went into the backyard to start my uncle's mind game.

"Throw me a few first so we can warm up," John said. After warming up John said, "Show me your fast ball."

Slade threw the first one and the sound of the ball hitting the glove left no doubt that he was fast.

"Go ahead, throw the fast ball," John said.

Looking stunned, Slade reared back and with extra effort, burned another pitch into John's glove.

"Is that the fastest you can throw?" John asked.

Slade just stood there dumbfounded as I did twenty years before him.

Taking his glove off, John threw it on the ground in front of him and said, "I won't need a glove to catch you. Throw the best you got, Slade," John said.

While my uncle got down in a crouch and held up his bare hands, Slade tried to protest. "Uncle John, you could hurt yourself."

"Come on, kid. That fastball you got could be timed with a calendar," John teased.

With his lips pursed and his eyes glaring, Slade reached back and launched the ball as hard as he could. The sound of rawhide hitting bone made the pounding sound of someone making hamburger patties.

"Not bad, kid, not bad. I sure hope you can hit," John said as he turned to the family and winked. Calmly, John walked over and stuck his hand in the ice chest of beer and made believe he was searching for a beer.

"You felt that! I know you did, Uncle John," said Slade.

"Right now I don't feel a thing," John said, as everyone started to laugh aloud.

I remember how deflated I felt when John did the same stunt to me when I was Slade's age. It was his signature in our family's memory bank, every boy in the family endured the show and never forgot the incident, or Uncle John. I suppose that was his idea all along. Remembrance.

It was March already and the holidays were only a faint memory. The first signs of spring were beginning to show with warmer weather, greener grass, and the tulips just breaking through the ground on the Park Avenue median. Downtown, spring brought with it the smells of a decaying neighborhood, and the added burden of policing thousands more on the street. Pimps, prostitutes, junkies, and assorted low lifes were beginning to get into each other's faces, and when you add drunken domino players to the mix, the explosives just need a spark to set it off. The stores from that December night were still boarded up and vacant. Junkies were using them for shooting galleries, and they were easy collars you wanted to get off the street. This was the time of the year when cops were more referee than cop.

I thought I deserved an Academy Award for best actor in a dramatic lead for walking alone on a beat with a smile on my face and a lump in my throat. Every cop learned to live with fear and do his job despite it, but it took its toll on us in so many other ways. The force had high incidences of divorce, alcoholism, and psychological problems. For a cop, the summer was just plain hell.

It was Friday, my last tour for this set of days, and JC and I had just returned from court.

"Officer Halley return from court, no meal LT," I said to the desk lieutenant.

"Same message Officer Colby," JC said.

"Just the men I wanted to see. The captain wants to see you forthwith in his office," Lieutenant Burns said.

"What the hell did you do now, JC?" I said jokingly.

"If I told you once, I have told you a thousand times—do not bury bodies in shallow graves," JC said.

Lieutenant Burns stepped down from behind the desk and knocked on the captain's door.

"Captain Mendelson, Halley and Colby are here. You still wanna see them?" Lieutenant Burns asked.

"Yeah. Send them in."

We walked through the captain's door like two schoolboys being brought to the principal's office. Outside the office, JC shoved me in first and his actions made me laugh.

"Well, I'm glad you're in such good humor, Halley," Captain Mendelson said.

Holding my hat under my arm and trying to stifle my nervous laugh, I said, "You asked to see us, Captain?"

"Yes. Come in and close the door, Colby."

"I've been noticing all the activity you two have been generating and I wanted to tell you personally what a great job I think you're doing. Also, we are starting a new crime program throughout the borough and we need eight active cops and one sergeant to ride in plainclothes in an unmarked car. They are calling it the "anti-crime unit" and you will work 10:00 a.m. to 6:00 p.m. and 6:00 p.m. to 2:00 a.m. in the precinct. Would you two be interested in the assignment?"

"Would we be able to make all the arrests we want to? I mean, even drug collars?" JC asked.

"As long as they were quality drug collars, not the one joint variety," Captain Mendolson said.

"Why don't the two of you talk it over and let me know before end of tour today."

I left the office with high hopes for this new assignment, but JC had some reservations about riding with a sergeant in the car all day. We both agreed that this was a volunteer assignment and we could both get out if we didn't like it. We were given the next three days off and were to start on Monday.

CHAPTER 9

I PUT ANNIE IN THE back seat with her favorite stuffed animals and Karen and I headed out to Long Island for a third look at a house she liked in Lake Ronkonkoma.

We had been to the house on different days, in the morning, afternoon, and now I was driving out there during rush hour to get the feel for it. The trip without traffic took only about fifty minutes, but today it took over an hour and ten minutes.

"You're three blocks away from the Long Island Expressway, four miles from the Long Island Railroad station, and about a mile from supermarkets and churches," Cherry Long, the broker, said.

"What kind of schools do they have out here?" Karen asked.

"The Sachem School District is the best in Suffolk County. They attract the best teachers and spend the most money per student in the county. All the Sachem schools are modern with large playgrounds for your children to grow with," Cherry said.

Karen looked at me with those deep blue eyes of hers and said, "What do you think, Michael?"

"I don't know, dear. Maybe we should discuss it a little bit," I said.

As we were going to the front door, Cherry's face took on a strange scowl when she spoke. "There is another, older couple coming to look at the house today. If you want, you can put a small deposit down on the house to keep it from being bought out from under you. The deposit is one hundred percent refundable."

Karen and I went outside the real estate office to talk it over.

"I love the house, Michael! Do you love it, too?" Karen asked.

"That crap about someone else being interested in the house is a ploy to get us to commit without us even haggling on the price," I said.

"Do you have any idea how heartbroken I will be if what she says is true and we lose this house over a little deposit?" Karen said.

The tone of her voice and the not so veiled threat had me reaching for the blank check that I had been carrying in my wallet for months.

"If you really think it's the house for us," I said sheepishly.

Karen took the check, kissed me on the cheek, and said, "I have a good feeling about this."

We sat in Cherry's office for another hour filling out paperwork and making a list of things we were required to do.

"Buying a house is a major milestone in a couple's life," Cherry said. "I will try to make the transition from renter to homeowner as pleasant as possible."

Cherry was the consummate businesswoman and she knew just what to say and who to say it to. She spoke to Karen about fixing up the house with her own style and color schemes. When she spoke to me it was to give me a number to call or paper to sign. I felt like a prize bull that had been used for stud and I was no longer needed for the process. On our way back to Queens, I kept wondering whether or not we could afford home ownership and how broke we would be after we took the plunge.

"I think we are going to be very happy in our new home, Michael," Karen said.

Looking at Karen's face light up when she talked about her new home convinced me that I had to let this dream of hers come true, no matter what the cost.

"Where the hell did all this traffic come from?" I mumbled.

"Please don't curse in front of Annie, Michael," Karen said.

"Sorry," I said.

I cursed silently all the way back to Queens in the bumper-to-bumper traffic.

CHAPTER *10*

THE WHITE PAPER CUP BLEW erratically across the darkened street while the traffic light clicked off its commands to an empty block. Easing out of the darkness, the blue Caddy moved slowly, deliberately toward the curb and stopped. Three men stepped onto the sidewalk and moved quickly toward the front door of the Avenue C Liquor Store. The driver kept the engine running and held his sawed-off shotgun in his lap. The store clerk watched helplessly as the three men shoved guns in his face and demanded the day's cash.

"Yes, sir...yes, sir. Don't shoot! Please, don't shoot!" said Ismael Ranni. Since coming to America from India, Ranni worked two jobs to help support his wife and new baby

The small muscular robber pushed Ranni out of the way and began shoving the cash from the register in his pockets. "Where is the safe?" the small robber demanded while pressing a snub-nosed revolver to the back of Ranni's head.

"On the floor under the carton of toothpaste," said Ranni.

The robber by the door was getting nervous and was anxious to leave.

"Come on, man, it's getting late."

"Yeah. Cap the fucker and let's book," said the robber.

Ranni's face turned ashen as he realized that these men meant to kill him.

"Please, I won't tell anybody!" Ranni said as he put his hands out in front of him and backed up against the counter.

"Please! I have a wife and a..."

Bang! Bang! The shots crashed into Ismael Ranni's head and in a flash of light the new father lay dead. The three killers quickly grabbed the cash and two bottles of Bacardi rum, and drove off. A witness would later say that she watched them give high fives to each other.

"This is the eighth stick-up this crew has committed, and eleven people have been murdered, leaving no witnesses and no clues. They have to be stopped!" said Captain James Stanley, Manhattan South Robbery Task Force.

"We have to fight fire with fire," said Detective Sergeant Olmire. "I think it's time we brought in the Stakeout Unit."

Captain Stanley frowned and then nodded agreement.

"Make sure a couple of our men are assigned to them whenever they work this borough."

Captain Stanley said, "Take them from the precinct, not the bureau."

It was my second 6:00 p.m. to 2:00 a.m. and JC had taken the night off for his son's birthday party. I wound up getting stuck with a new sergeant from the police academy who was just doing patrol work for his probation. Sergeant Royce was in his last year of law school at NYU and he definitely didn't have the stones for patrol. He was tall and painfully thin, with a nervous twitch in his right eye whenever we got close to any action.

While passing Avenue D and 7th Street a beer bottle bounced off the roof of our unmarked car.

"Oh, my God! What the hell was that?" Sergeant Royce yelled.

Unable to contain myself, I began to laugh uncontrollably at Royce's fear.

"Don't worry, Sarge, you never hear the one that kills you," I said while roaring with laughter. Every time I tried to get the laughter under control, I would see his right eye twitching like the caution light on a Con Edison "Dig we must" sign and that would start me all over again.

"I have some paper work to do, so take me back to the house." Royce said with a controlled rage.

I drove him back to the station house, and to this day I have never seen or heard of him since. I know it seemed heartless, but these smart asses never wanted to be cops—they just wanted a free college ride through the department. They worked days at headquarters and went to school full time. The department bent over backward to allow cops to get an education. Most of them quit once they got the degree. I felt they should put their time on the front lines to wear that badge, education or not.

There was nobody available to ride with me until after 10:00 p.m. so I took an early meal period and began filling my brief case with forms, temporary operating orders, standard operating orders, and various wanted posters. One posting, obscured with wanted signs, read "Wanted, volunteers from precinct to work with Stakeout Unit. See Capt. Stanley." Manhattan South Robbery Squad. I gave the number a ring and to my surprise, Captain Stanley took my call and seemed genuinely glad to hear from me. I gave him my name and JC's and told him we would be available whenever the need arose.

"If we decide to work your precinct, Halley, we'll reach out to you and your partner. Until then, good luck," Captain Stanley said.

When I told JC the following night, he wasn't thrilled.

"What the hell were you thinking, Mike? Do you know anything about the Stakeout Unit?" JC asked.

"No, I just thought it would be a change of pace for us, that's all," I said.

"Let me enlighten you, Michael," JC said. "They sit on possible targets for armed robberies, places that have been hit in the past, and they pray that they get hit again. If these guys lived a hundred years ago, they would have been the gunfighters in Dodge City or Tombstone. They even have pet names for their guns, man!"

"Yeah, sure, JC! You expect me to believe that shit?" I said.

"Just pray we don't get the call, that's all."

CHAPTER *11*

IT WAS THE SIXTH OF June and the rain was coming down in buckets all morning long. JC and I were just pulling up to the station house when we spotted Oliveri and his partner, Dave Walden, dragging someone along the ground.

"Are they locking up a cop?" JC asked Sergeant Kenny.

"No. That's a meter maid who gave Oliveri some lip up on 14th Street."

"Really! What a set of balls," JC said. "His uniform could pass for ours."

"Yeah, this ticket feud is heating up, and their supervisors can't seem to calm them down," said Sergeant Kenny. "People are calling ten-thirteens on them cause they think they're cops."

Oliveri dragged the man up the three steps to the station house and dropped his handcuffed body in front of the desk.

"What's this, Officer?" asked Lieutenant Corrigan.

"One for resisting and interference with governmental administration," Oliveri said. After relating the story of the arrest to the desk officer, Oliveri took his arrest upstairs to the detective squad. The station was becoming overrun with reporters and city officials wanting to know what was going on.

The city needed new revenue and had hired parking enforcement agents to generate money through summons activity. The agents ticketed indiscriminately without regard to the circumstances or people involved.

The deputy mayor and the Parking Enforcement commissioner pulled up in separate cars and immediately went into the captain's office. Their voices could be heard throughout the station house when the mayor began screaming.

"These brain-dead assholes are a public relations nightmare, Commissioner! What are you going to do about it?" Deputy Mayor Isaacs said.

"We have been training them on a daily basis about using common sense when issuing tickets," Commissioner Phelps said respectfully. "But they seem to ignore everything we tell them."

"If they don't listen to you, maybe we should find someone they will listen to," Isaacs said.

"You have thirty days to get them to follow the spirit of the law instead of the letter of the law.

After that, you better update your resume, because you'll be gone. Do you understand?"

"Yes, sir, I understand," Phelps said.

"Send in the precinct commander on your way out, Phelps," ordered Isaacs.

"Don't you two have something to do?" Sergeant Boyle asked JC and me. "Other than eavesdropping."

"We're on our way, boss," JC said.

As we sat in the backroom copying the alarms of the day off the Teletype machine, JC handed me an envelope and said, "Here is the first installment of the money I owe you."

Taking the envelope, I said, "Can you afford this?"

"I'll give you some each payday until I can float a loan from the Municipal Credit Union."

JC had been on a tear for the past few weeks making collars and banking the overtime. In the short time we had been together in plainclothes I had come to realize he was a hell of a cop when he wanted to be. Since winning his case against his wife in court, JC was seeing his son every chance he got. Both JC and his wife were playing the buying game now, trying to win the love of their child. The divorce seemed harder on JC than his wife, but it created a war zone around his son, and the few times I met him the kid was very nervous.

"Did you hear what happened to Senator Kennedy tonight?" Sergeant Boyle asked.

"No, did he find Jimmy Hoffa?" JC quipped.

"He just got shot by some Arab out in California," Boyle said.

"They sure got it in for the Kennedys! How the hell did this guy get close enough to do this?" JC asked.

"This Palestinian left some kind of diary that the FBI is looking at," Boyle said.

"How convenient," I said. "Oswald left a diary, too, after he assassinated John Kennedy."

"Yeah, the diary leaves no loose ends. No conspiracy theory, and no smoking gun from the grassy knoll. What a tidy little murder," JC said.

"Rosy Grier, you know, the football player, tackled the little bastard in the kitchen of the hotel," Boyle said.

"Where were his bodyguards, or the cops for that matter?" I said.

"It would never happen in New York. Too many cops to go through for one thing, and we've been doing it longer."

"Bite your tongue, man. We've got the pope coming soon," JC said.

It was close to eight o'clock when we spotted two men enter and leave several hallways on the block.

"What do you think...junkies or burglars?" JC asked.

"Look! They came back out and went into another building," I said. "Burglars, I think."

Leaving the car, JC and I moved close to the building line and began trotting toward the row of buildings we last saw our targets.

'Hello. Who's there?"

"Medar Meda."

The buzzers were already ringing off the hook in the hallway of 230 East 5th Street.

"They got in already. We'll try the top floor," JC said.

Holding the door until it quietly closed, JC put his index finger to his lips to signal silence, and with his other hand motioned me to the foot of the stairs.

"Wait until we hear the roof door open, then we'll go," JC whispered.

After hearing the door slam, we began the climb, taking two steps at a time, staying close to the wall in case they were looking down the flight of stairs. We rested on the fourth-floor landing to catch our breath so we wouldn't be too winded if we had to face off with these guys. Reaching the sixth floor, I started to climb to the roof, but JC grabbed my arm and said, "Not the roof. We'll get them through the apartment," JC whispered.

"Which apartment?" I asked.

"It has to be the apartment facing the rear courtyard. That's either 6C or 6D," JC said.

JC motioned to me with his left hand cupped over his ear to listen at the door of one apartment while I listened at the other. The sound of breaking glass was very faint, but it was coming from apartment 6C.

"What now?" I said excitedly.

"Now we wait," JC said.

Standing in the hallway smoking a cigarette while two burglars ransacked an apartment seemed bizarre to me and I said, "This is nuts! Let's kick the door down and go in before they get away."

"The two of us will never catch these guys without more men, and right now we're it," JC said. "Shhhh. Patience, Mike."

While standing on both sides of the apartment door, we could hear the muffled sounds of other residents going about their daily lives without a clue that their neighbor was losing all he owned.

Click-clack. The tumblers on the locked apartment moved and the door slowly swung open. The first thing through the door was a white pillowcase followed by an arm that JC grabbed quickly and yanked into the hallway.

"HEY, MUDDER FUCKER!" perp one yelled.

"Policia! Freeze!" JC said as he quickly wrestled the surprised burglar to the ground and cuffed both his wrists.

The second perp turned and tried to make it to the fire escape window but tripped over a television set they had left in the middle of the hall. I was on top of him before he could regain his feet and tried to pull his arm around his back.

"You're under arrest, amigo!" I shouted.

Twisting around with his free hand, he plunged a knife into my left arm.

"Ow, you crummy bastard," I yelled. I pinned his free arm with my leg and forced him to drop the blade by shoving his other arm up to the small of his back.

"Okay, Okay! I geeve up man! No mas, man," perp two said.

While walking the prisoners down the stairs JC asked, "What the hell is that blood from, Mike?"

"This son of a bitch stabbed me with a knife," I said while looking at the puncture.

The knife wielder began to smile as we talked, and JC grabbed him by the shoulder and said, "You think stabbing a cop is funny?"

The prisoner was still smiling when JC shoved him down a flight of stairs. Tumbling and screaming, the prisoner landed in a heap at the landing and immediately began calling for help.

"The police are trying to kill me! Stop them. Please help me."

"You know, amigo, there are three more flights of stairs and I don't know how your luck is gonna hold up, so you better get ready to meet your maker," JC said.

"Wait man! Wait! I got information you need! Let's trade."

Looking at me and holding the prisoner near the first step, JC said, "I'll give you five to one odds he doesn't bounce so good this time."

"NO. NO. Wait. I know who killed that cop a while ago."

"You'd say anything not to take the ride, scumhead," JC said.

"What cop you talking about?" I asked.

"Anselmo."

CHAPTER *12*

WE DRAGGED BOTH PRISONERS DOWN the stairs and into the basement of the building near the fuse boxes in the rear. Pulling out two rusted folding chairs from the property bin, JC sat both men down forcefully.

"We are gonna ask you some questions now and I hope for your sake that you are gonna be truthful cause no one will hear you scream from down here," I said.

Both men just nodded their heads in agreement.

"What's your name?"

"I'm Manuel Rodriguez. This is Jose Fuentes. He doesn't know anything about what I'm going to tell you...you know...about that cop's murder," Rodriguez said.

"Let's hear what you know," I said.

"He's trying to get out of falling down some stairs," JC said.

"No. I have information, but I want protection, and not from you city cops, either. I want the Feds and the Witness Protection Program," Rodriguez said.

"Why the Feds?" I asked. "This is a city matter."

"I want a good lawyer, too, like Kuntsler or F. Lee Bailey. No legal aid clowns for me, man.

What I know will sink a lot of bad dudes and my ass will be grass if they get to me," Rodriguez said.

Laughing out loud, JC squeezed Rodriguez's cheeks and said, "You keep playing us and all you're going to need is an embalmer."

"I know the guy who did the shooting, man," Rodriguez said.

"You're gonna get us killed!" Fuentes yelled.

JC pulled Fuentes out of his chair and threw him across the cement floor.

"You're facing twenty-five years for stabbing a cop during a first-degree burglary. Hell, you'll be collecting Social Security when you two get out," JC said.

"Who did it?" I asked.

"It was that big motherfukin' cop Oliveri," Rodriguez said. "Now you see why I need protection."

"Oh, man, we're as good as dead now," Fuentes said.

Both JC and I were standing there in the basement with a lost look in our eyes when I asked, "How do you know? Were you there? Did you see it done?"

"Let's just say I'm involved. I'm not saying another word until I get representation," Rodriguez said.

"You're full of shit!" JC said.

"Let's book them, Mike, and say sayonara."

"He told me to get rid of the gun, but I kept it just in case. It probably has his prints on it,"

Rodriguez said.

"Where is the gun?" I asked.

"A man named Chase is keeping it safe," Rodriguez said. "Do we deal?"

"Why was Anselmo killed?" I asked.

"He was getting too close to Oliveri and our little operation," Rodriguez said. "I'll spill once my deal is in writing."

"I'm sure the DA will agree to this deal, that is, if you can produce evidence," I said.

"Don't you worry man...what I got is A number one," Rodriguez said. "One more thing, though, before we go anywhere. I need for you to let Fuentes go. He's my brother-in-law and my sister can't afford to lose us both because she's got four kids to feed. I'll take the weight for everything. Please, if you let him go, nobody will know about him or how much he knows. Once I'm gone, my sister will need all the help she can get," Rodriguez said.

JC and I both looked at each other, and while I shrugged my shoulders, JC moved to Fuentes and unlocked his handcuffs.

"As long as you keep your mouth shut you stay alive," JC said to Fuentes.

Rubbing his wrists and backing toward the cellar stairs, Fuentes said, "Thank you, Manny."

"Hang tough, man, and don't worry about Maria."

CHAPTER *13*

JC AND I HAD LODGED Rodriguez in a holding cell downstairs while we made notifications to the borough commander, duty captain, and Internal Affairs.

Captain James Luzinsky was the duty captain for Manhattan South on this night and he was the first to arrive. We brought him up to speed with what Rodriguez told us and he seemed fine until we told him about Oliveri.

"A cop! Oh, brother. Did you notify IAD?" Luzinsky said. "The shit is gonna hit the fan over this! Where is he?"

"In the cells," JC said.

"Let's go talk to him," Luzinsky said.

Approaching the small cell block, JC let out a yell. "Oh, my God! That stupid son of a bitch." JC quickly opened the cell door and grabbed Rodriguez's legs as they dangled in midair. "Quick! Cut him down," JC ordered.

His body fell lifeless into our arms as we tried to find a pulse.

"Don't throw those laces away. That's evidence," Luzinsky ordered.

"Where the hell did these laces come from? We took his belt and laces and vouchered them," I said.

The ambulance attendants pronounced Rodriguez DOA and all the brass were scurrying around trying to pass the buck of responsibility.

"Whale shit falls to the bottom of the ocean and that's where we are in the grand scheme of things," JC said. "We're gonna get jammed up for this one, but good."

"Why do you say that?" I asked.

"He was our prisoner and we were responsible for his well-being," JC said.

"I searched him real good and he didn't have a dam thing on him, let alone shoelaces," I said.

"I searched him too and he was clean," said Lenny Joyce. Joyce was on light duty and was assigned to the "broom" or station house maintenance. The cells were part of his responsibility, especially when they were occupied. "You guys didn't tell me he was a suicide watch."

"He wasn't, Lenny! He had information about Anselmo's murder," I said. "He was a material witness, not some guy freaking out over his arrest."

"He didn't sound normal when he began screaming for someone to let him out," Joyce said. "When was that?" I asked.

"A little after you put him in. Hell, he didn't shut up until Oliveri warned him," Joyce said. "Oliveri! Oliveri came to see him?" JC yelled. "How long was he here?"

"They covered for me for a few minutes while I went next door for a cold one," Joyce said. "They took off when I got back."

"They? Oliveri and who else?" I asked.

"You know, his partner Walden."

"Did you check on Rodriguez when you got back?" I asked.

"No. Oliveri said he was sleeping and I didn't need to climb the stairs with my bad knees," Joyce said.

Joyce began climbing back up the basement stairs one by one in obvious pain. As he closed the basement door, JC and I looked at each other and I said, "Well, what now?"

"You know the bastard murdered Rodriguez and we can't prove a damn thing. That dopey halfwit Joyce is half in the bag and none of what he told us will stand up in court," JC said.

"We'll have to tell the story to Internal Affairs and let them worry about it," I said. "So, let's sign out and figure out what comes next."

As JC and I walked to our cars on the corner of the station house blocks, Oliveri stepped out of a hallway and in front of our path.

"You know, cops shouldn't believe everything a low life fucker like Rodriguez tells them. Look at all the trouble that mutt caused," Oliveri said. "Don't you two have enough enemies on the street without making more?"

"Is that a threat?" JC asked.

Moving close to JC's face, Oliveri smirked and said, "Just advice to live by. With the key word being live."

Oliveri deliberately bumped into JC as he walked past him and headed down the block to the station house. As I watched Oliveri fade into the unlit street, a chill ran down my spine and made me shiver suddenly.

"You know, I don't think I ever met anyone without a conscience before. He murders without giving it a second thought," I said.

"That son of a bitch means to add us to the list," JC said. "I just don't understand why he warned us."

"After what we told Internal Affairs tonight, they would go right after him if we turned up dead," I said.

"Those rejects couldn't find an elephant in a phone booth and Oliveri knows it," JC said. "It's up to us to bury this guy before he does it to us."

"Look, I'll see you tomorrow and we'll talk about it some more. Right now I'm dead on my feet," I said.

"Don't use that word, it might give that Neanderthal ideas," JC said. "See you at four."

As I drove across the Brooklyn Bridge the warm ocean breeze felt good on my face and for a few minutes made me forget my troubles. So many questions were still running through my head, like voices in a courtroom.

"Why did Oliveri murder two people? What was he doing that warranted murdering someone?"

I mumbled. "How many people were in it with Oliveri?" The real question for me, though, was what was I going to do about it? I knew that sooner or later, Oliveri would have to make a move on JC and me, so I had better figure out a plan pronto.

CHAPTER 14

IT WAS WELL AFTER TWO in the morning when I exited the Queens Borough Bridge and headed down 31ˢᵗ Avenue for some breakfast. The diner was a small hash and eggs place under the elevated subway. The screeching brakes of trains and the oddballs prowling the streets at that time of the morning gave the place a surreal feeling. I grabbed a stool at the rear of the counter, so I could have time to react if somebody tried to rob the place. After giving the counter man my order of bacon and eggs, I sat back and began sipping my coffee.

Two black men entered the diner and ordered two coffees to go. While the two men waited near the cash register, a short, muscular white man staggered up behind them and said, "Give me coffee, light and sweet, to go."

"As soon as I'm done with these gentlemen," said the counter man.

"I'm white and I come first over these niggers," slurred the drunk.

Before the echo of his words had died out, the younger of the two black men punched the drunk square in the mouth. The force of the blow knocked a piece of the drunk's tooth on to my English muffin. I eased my Smith and Wesson snub nose from my ankle holster and held it alongside my right leg out of sight.

The drunk bounced up quickly from the floor and seemed eager to fight. Suddenly, holding both his hands up in the air, he turned and ran out the door. The older of the two black men had pulled a small caliber automatic and was waving it around in no particular direction.

"We just want some coffee," the older man said.

The counter man gave them their two coffees and the men left three dollars on the counter. I watched the two men back out the door and speed away in an old, dark Caddy. After following them outside, I watched their lights grow dim in the distance. A feeling of shame swept over me as I stood on the sidewalk. Shame for my race and what hate can turn people into.

"A lousy cup of coffee is all they wanted," I murmured.

Looking at the counter man I said, "How much do I owe you?"

"Forget it. It's on the house," said the counter man.

I slipped a couple of bucks by the register and said, "You should ask your boss for a raise or better hours."

I didn't wait for a reply but headed home for some much-needed rest. I also made a mental note not to stop for breakfast anymore.

The following morning, I called JC and told him to meet me early on 14th Street near Broadway before we reported for duty. Coming up out of the subway I could see the annoyance on JC's face as he approached.

"Why do we have to meet before three o'clock?" JC asked.

"Where is your car?" I asked.

"At the station house. I hopped the subway," JC answered.

"Do you remember Rodriguez saying that the gun used in the homicide was safe and it was being held by a guy named Chase?" I asked.

"Yeah. What about it?" JC said.

'I think the Chase he was talking about is across the street. At that Chase bank," I said pointing to the bank. "Maybe in a safe deposit box," I continued.

JC's face began to beam, and he patted me on the shoulder and said, "You know you may be onto something. But how do we get our hands on it if it's in a locked box?"

"They won't let us look at it without a search warrant, but they might let us know if there is a box in his name," I said. "Once we get that, IAD can get the warrant."

"Well, what the hell are we standing here for? Let's do it," JC said.

My hunch was right. There was a safety deposit box in Rodriguez's name. It was opened two days after Anselmo's murder.

"I think we should call Internal Affairs from an outside line and set up a meet," JC said. "Can't trust anyone at the station."

"You really think other cops are involved?" I asked.

"I'm not taking any chances with this info. Somebody told Oliveri that we brought in Rodriguez the day he got hanged," JC said.

"Loose lips sink ships, Mike, so let's play it safe."

After calling IAD on Poplar Street in Brooklyn and setting up a confidential meeting, we headed into the precinct for a 4 to 12 tour.

"IAD called and wants the both of you at their office at five tonight. Do you know what it's about?" Sergeant Boyce asked.

"It's probably about the hanging of our prisoner," I said.

"Okay. Take RMP #1423 and go there in uniform. We'll use somebody else in the anti-crime sector," Sergeant Boyce ordered. "Your post change is at 1615."

The IAD bosses were ecstatic about the information we gave them, and while we sat in their office speaking into their tape recorders, they were already enroute to the bank with a warrant.

"After your material witness was found hanged, what did you do next?" Captain Sylvester asked.

"We spoke to the broom and he told us that Oliveri and his partner were babysitting Rodriguez while he went for a drink," I said. I left out the fact that the drink was a beer.

"The broom didn't know that Rodriguez was going to rat on Oliveri for murder. We kept it quiet until we could notify you guys," JC said. "Oliveri and his partner were notified by someone in the station house, else why would they be in two hours before their tour."

"You men have done a great job so far, now we want you to do more. We want the both of you to wear a wire and try to make a deal with these rogue cops," Captain Sylvester said.

"A wire! He'll know right away that we're setting them up, " JC said.

"Not if you tell them you want to be cut in on the action, whatever that is," Captain Sylvester said.

"Two men are dead already trying to fuck with these guys. I don't want to add to the list," JC said.

"We'll be right with you every step of the way. Besides, these bastards killed your friend," Captain Sylvester said. "Don't you want justice?"

"To hell with justice. I want revenge," I said.

CHAPTER 15

EARLY THE FOLLOWING MORNING THE sound of my phone ringing woke me out of a deep sleep.

"Hello," I answered sleepily.

"Officer Halley, this is Captain Sylvester. I have some bad news for you."

"What?" I asked.

"The gun is the one used in the murder, but it has no prints. We have no way to link the gun to Oliveri or Walden. The serial number is registered to a gun shop in Virginia and was reported stolen two years ago," Captain Sylvester said.

"What happens now?" I asked.

"We'll continue to watch Oliveri and his partner, but frankly, without more to go on, we are dead in the water. Unless, of course, you or your partner have changed your mind about wearing a wire?" Captain Sylvester asked.

"Without leverage why would he even talk to us now?" I asked.

"He doesn't know the gun has no links to him. Maybe that might push his buttons," Captain

Sylvester said. "Whatever you decide, let me know ASAP."

"I need to do some thinking, Captain, so I'll have to let you know," I said.

"Stay in touch, Halley," Sylvester said.

I called JC on a pay phone, so Karen wouldn't hear me talk. She would be able to tell right away that there was something wrong, and what with our moving in a few weeks, she had enough to worry about. JC was pissed about the gun but was livid that Captain Sylvester didn't call him also.

"You'd think he would have the common courtesy to notify me as well as you!" JC said.

"I guess he figured I would pass along the information to you," I said.

"Did he bring up the wire bullshit again?" JC asked.

"Yeah, he did. I told him I'd have to think about it," I said.

"That's why he called you. You're vacillating about wearing the lousy wire and they know it,"

JC said.

"A couple of nights ago you stood on the corner and spoke about killing Oliveri. Now you balk at wearing a wire to catch a murderer. I don't get it," I said.

"Wearing a wire is what rats do. It just rubs me the wrong way, that's all. Putting a bullet through his head is the manlier thing to do," JC said.

"You're a sick puppy, JC. You need some professional help. Murder over justice?" I said.

"Ask Anselmo's family which way they would like us to go and I'll bet you dollars to donuts they go my way," JC said. "In your heart you know I'm right."

"Once you step over the line, there would be nothing separating us from the Oliveri's of the world," I said.

"Hell, Mike, you murdered VC over in Nam because they were trying to kill you. Oliveri is trying to kill you too, but you say there is a difference? What difference?" JC asked.

"Other than the obvious fact that Viet Nam was war, the bullets were already bouncing around my head when I killed. It was self-defense," I said. "Oliveri has only made threats."

"All right, all right. What's next then?" JC asked.

"I'll see you at six tonight and we'll talk then," I said.

"Yeah, right. Blah, blah, blah." *Click.* JC ended the conversation.

It was pouring rain at six that night when JC and I began touring the precinct sectors.

"Nobody is on the street. We'll have to make some car stops if we're gonna collar up tonight." JC said.

"I was wondering. Do you still have that arrest report you began on Rodriguez?" I asked.

"It's incomplete because we didn't go through with the burglary collar," JC said.

"Do you still have it?" I asked.

Reaching over the back seat, JC pulled his attaché case onto his lap and began looking through his paperwork.

"Here it is," JC said as he handed me the UF#61. "What are you looking for?"

"This!" I said, pointing to the sheet listing known relatives.

"Fuentes, 635 East 9th Street," JC read. "FUENTES!"

"I bet that SOB knows plenty. Remember when his brother-in-law gave us Oliveri's name. He almost shit a brick!" JC exclaimed. "Let's get him!"

"Don't you think we should include the rat squad?" I asked.

"First, let's see if he's still at that address. He could be halfway around the world by now after his brother-in-law's death," JC said. "We can notify them after we have something concrete."

We gave the block a drive by and the whole neighborhood seemed deserted. Parking the car on Avenue D, we made our way through the downpour and into the building.

"Apartment 1C is just down the hall, so maybe one of us should cover the back," JC said.

"I'll take the back," I said.

JC watched me as I opened the rear door and headed down the metal stairs into the rear yard.

After I nodded to him that I was in position, he turned and walked toward the apartment. There was a rear window open as a curtain was blowing through it. I tried to move as close to it as possible.

"OPEN UP. POLICIA!" JC yelled.

A foot, then a torso, and finally the rest of Jose Fuentes hung from the window and dropped to the ground.

"Freeze.," I said.

"You mother fuckers! I knew you couldn't be trusted!" Fuentes said. "You can't make a deal with you pigs." In his waistband Fuentes had a small caliber automatic.

"What's this, Fuentes?" I asked while holding the gun.

"That's my life insurance," Fuentes said. "You assholes couldn't protect Manny so I figured I better do it myself."

"If it was Oliveri who knocked on your door, you'd be dead now," I said.

JC appeared on the stairs and said for us to go back into the apartment. Fuentes's wife Maria was crying and so were her kids.

"Why can't you leave us alone? First you get my brother killed, now you want to kill my husband," Maria cried.

"We're here to try to protect you and your husband, Mana. A cop named Oliveri is eliminating anyone who knows about him and what he has done," JC said.

Looking at her husband, Maria Fuentes asked Jose, "Is this true what they say?"

"It's true," said Jose, looking toward the ground. "I'm sorry, Maria."

She pulled a kitchen chair out from the table and sat down. She began to sob while holding her head in her hands.

"What is going to become of us?" Maria cried. "How will I feed my babies without you and Manny?" Maria asked Jose.

Jose Fuentes's shoulders began to sag, and he too began to cry.

I...I am... very...sorry, Maria," Jose balled.

It took us awhile to calm down the Fuentes family, but once that was done, JC took control.

"We don't want to arrest your husband. We need him to tell us all he knows about this deal your brother and this cop had going. We believe your brother was murdered by this cop and he won't hesitate to kill again," JC said.

"My brother didn't commit suicide?" Maria asked.

"We don't think so. We can't prove it right now, but with your husband's help we might have a chance," JC said. "What do you say, will you help us bring Manny's killer to justice?"

"You tell what you know, Jose. Please," Maria begged. Jose wouldn't look at her while she was staring at him.

Shaking his head, he said, "They will kill us if I talk."

"If you don't tell what you know, you are no man. YOU ARE A COWARD!" Maria yelled.

Jose stopped crying and looked up at his wife and said, "How could you say that about me, Maria? Haven't I given you everything you ever wanted?"

"I will not have my children shamed by living with a coward. My brother's death must be avenged. If you won't do it, I will find someone who is man enough to do this for me," Maria said.

Jose sat down on the arm of a couch in the adjoining living room and began wiping his eyes.

He cleared his throat, stood up, and said, "What do you want to know?"

CHAPTER 16

FUENTES BEGAN TELLING HIS STORY to us in a very matter-of-fact way while JC and I stood listening with our mouths wide open. Oliveri and his partner Walden were the ones that Fuentes dealt with, but he said he had hard evidence on other cops involved.

"What are the names of the other cops?" I asked.

"Manny knew the higher ups who gave Oliveri orders, but I don't know their names," Fuentes said. "Manny had paperwork and pictures of these fuckers when they met last month for the payoffs on some of our jobs. Poor Manny thought they would be his insurance against these rat bastards."

"Where are the pictures?" JC asked.

"In a locker in Grand Central Station. That's where he met them last time," Fuentes said.

"Just what were you guys doing?" I asked.

"All I know is that we were given places to rob, and we would go there, and they would have a shitload of jewelry. Sometimes it was in cars, hotel rooms, and one time it was a safety deposit box. It was all top-quality stuff, man. Prime shit," Fuentes said.

"Did you or Manny fence the stuff?" JC asked.

"No way, man. Right after the heist we would meet Oliveri close by the job and we gave the stuff to him right away. One time some security guard spotted us, and he was chasing us when Oliveri showed up and took over the chase for the guard," Fuentes said.

"They ran interference for you and Manny then?" JC asked.

Never got caught and the dinero was great," Fuentes said.

"These burglaries were they all in our precinct?" I asked.

"All over Manhattan," Fuentes said.

"Knowing you and Manny, how much of that jewelry did you skim off the top?" I asked.

"Just a few pieces from each job. Manny put it with the pictures for proof," Fuentes said.

"Weren't you afraid Oliveri or his boss would find out and blow your head off?" I asked.

"Manny thought since we weren't going to fence it, we would just say that the jewelers we ripped off were padding the insurance bill," Fuentes said.

"They were all jewelers?" JC asked.

"We read about some of the jobs in the paper and they were all jewelry salesmen we ripped off."

Fuentes said.

"How the hell could Oliveri get access to that kind of information?" JC asked.

"Oliveri is the muscle. The brains of this outfit must be using police databases to identify jewelry salesmen and to determine the best places to set up the theft," I said.

"Hell, I didn't even know we could do that!" JC exclaimed.

"Only someone high up in the department would be able to get that kind of information. Someone in the detective division," I said.

"Why the squad?" JC asked.

"Access to that information would be on a need to know basis and jewelry salesmen's movements would only be useful to detectives in that precinct for intelligence purposes," I said.

"Do you have the key to the locker, Fuentes?" I asked.

"Yes, here on my key ring," Fuentes said.

Moving near him I unhooked the locker key, number 33, from the ring and placed it on my own key ring.

"I think we better get to that locker ASAP," JC said.

We took the cuffs off Fuentes and headed out the front door. The rain was still pelting the street when we got to the car and opened the door. Fuentes cried out and fell to the ground. Blood was pouring out from his neck and chest. I instinctively hit the ground just as another shot smashed into the car window and rained glass down on my back.

"You lousy fucks!" JC screamed. "They're using silencers!"

I watched JC crawl around from the front of the car to where I was lying. He had blood seeping from his side.

"You're hit!" I said.

"So are you," JC said while pointing to my side.

"Did you see them?" I asked.

"No. The shots came from the hallway across the street," JC said. "How is Fuentes?"

"He won't be testifying," I said. "We can't stay here. We have to move before they rush us."

"I think we should run in two different directions. Maybe we can get lucky and one of us will be able to make it out of here," JC said.

"Okay. I'll try for the alley near Avenue D. You try for that doorway by the wrought-iron fence," I said.

JC nodded his head as he tried to raise himself to his right knee and said, "We'll go on the count of three. One...two...three!" JC grunted.

We both stood up and began running in a crouch. I could hear the bullets whistling all around me as glass windows and pieces of concrete were being shattered. I kept running straight for the alley, praying I would make it before I got hit again. Turning into the alley I quickly glanced over my shoulder and could see two men chasing JC with only one behind me. I ducked behind a dumpster and into a doorway. I tried the doorknob on the steel door, but it was locked. I began to slide down to the wet pavement as my side was beginning to throb. Reaching for my side, I felt the warm, red blood oozing from a bullet hole. I stuck my finger into the wound, front and back, and knew the bullet had gone through my side. After sticking a handkerchief into the wound, I tied my belt around it to keep it in place.

After a while I stood up and looked out toward the street. It had been awhile since I had heard any shooting. As the lights of a passing car hit the end of the alley, I could see the outline of a man pull back away from the alley entrance.

"So, you're still out there. Well, I'm gonna have to do something before you get position on me,"

I mumbled.

Looking around the alley I could see the outline of a fire escape ladder directly above my head. Sticking my gun into my right front pocket, I climbed up on the garbage dumpster, staying close to the wall, and grabbed hold of the ladder and pulled myself onto it. I grunted quietly as the hole in my side seemed to tear as I exerted myself. I began to climb to the first landing and lay down to survey the alley. Another figure appeared at the entrance and began peering down the alley.

"Are you sure he went into the alley?" one of the shooters said.

"I'm sure he went in and didn't come out. There's a blood trail leading in," the second shooter said.

"He could be dead in there while we sit out here," the first shooter said. "Let's finish the job."

They began moving down the alley on both sides near the walls. I began to feel lightheaded, probably from loss of blood. If I tried to climb the ladder I'd be a sitting duck, and this landing was a poor vantage point. Throwing caution to the wind, I knelt on the iron landing, poked my gun through the slats, and fired two quick bursts at the shooter near the dumpster. I fired two more shots at the shooter in the open. I fell to the landing after the shots and waited for return fire. There was silence from below.

Cautiously, I raised my head and peered through the bars. I could make out a figure lying on the ground near the dumpster and one across from him. Neither man was moving. I wondered if I had been lucky enough to hit both shooters, or were they playing possum. I stepped over the rail and reached for the ladder. *Bang! Bang!* Two shots spit off the ladder I was holding, causing me to let go and drop to the ground. I hit hard and was slightly disoriented while struggling to get to my feet.

"Turn around, Halley. I don't want to give it to you in the back."

As I turned I saw Oliveri standing in front of me, bleeding from his stomach.

"You're a pretty fair shot, Hailey, but now it's your turn to feel the heat of a bullet," Oliveri said.

He raised the gun while his hand trembled and aimed at my head. *Bang! Bang! Bang!* The shots echoed loudly in the alley as I grimaced. Oliveri staggered to his right, dropped his gun, and fell backward, splashing into a large puddle of water.

"All that kung fu shit didn't help stop a thirty-eight, you muscle-bound asshole," JC said.

"It's about time you got here. I could've bled to death waiting for you," I joked. "What happened to the other shooters?"

"They lost me on Avenue D and I doubled back looking for you," JC said. "Good thing, too, or else I'd have to start breaking in a new partner."

Grabbing me under the shoulder, JC began carrying me out to the street where we could hear sirens in the distance.

CHAPTER 17

"HOW DO YOU FEEL TODAY?" Karen asked as she pulled back the curtains and raised the blinds to the bedroom.

"Okay," I mumbled while rubbing my eyes and stretching.

"Watch out you don't open your stitches," Karen said. "Get dressed and come for breakfast."

"Come for breakfast?" I whined.

"You're getting the stitches out today and nurse Karen is officially off duty," Karen said. It had been two weeks since the shooting and I had been out sick since coming home from the hospital.

"Any calls?" I asked.

"The district attorney's office called about the deposition you gave at the hospital. More questions I expect."

"How about JC?" I asked.

"He is doing fine and said he will meet you at the police surgeon's office today," Karen said.

"You want me to drive you or can you do it yourself?" Karen asked.

"I'll drive. You need to get out of the house for a while," I said.

Karen had hovered over me for two weeks and I knew she was a lot more worried about me than she was willing to let on. My body had been racked by infection and I was out of it for a few days. Even as I sat at the kitchen table I could feel my strength slipping away.

"After you see the surgeon, you get your butt right back home and into bed before you have a relapse," Karen said.

There was just a slight quiver in her voice when she spoke as if trying to hold back the tears. I knew my getting shot shook her up pretty good, but she was holding all her feelings inside.

"I'll come right home, I promise," I said.

I kissed her on the cheek and headed out the door. The surgeon was on Park Avenue on the Upper East Side of Manhattan. Doctor Ferguson was an honorary police surgeon who liked cops and was listed in *Who's Who of MDs*.

In the doctor's office, a woman sitting across from me wore a floor-length mink coat, had blue hair, and enough makeup on to give her the look of a practice corpse at Maloney's funeral parlor.

"Don't you sass me, you bad boy," the woman said to her poodle, who was staring at me and growling softly.

"You've got some nerve, lady, bringing that hairball into a doctor's office," I mumbled.

The woman refused to look in my direction and continued to scold the dog for his bad behavior. While she was talking to the dog I made a deliberate and sudden move of my arm, which sent the dog into a frenzy of barking, whining, and biting of the fur coat. The woman grabbed the dog and held it on her shoulder with her back to me. I feigned the same attack again and this time the woman and dog fell to the ground in a life and death struggle.

"Oh, my goodness!" yelled the receptionist. "Are you all right, Mrs. Stein?"

"I...I don't know what happened. Poopsie just doesn't like low-class people and becomes frightened when she sees one," the old woman said while moving her head in my direction.

Without my seeing him in all this excitement, JC had entered the office and seen what I did and was laughing quietly.

"That poor dog just had a very loose bowel movement on the rug, lady, and I think you fell in it," JC said.

Throwing the dog onto the leather couch, the woman pulled off her coat while screaming for help.

"Get it off! Get it off! Please...help me," the woman screamed hysterically.

"That's okay, lady, it's gone now. Either the dog ate it or it was crushed into the coat," JC said.

The old lady grabbed the dog and ran out the door.

"What do you suppose got into that dog?" asked the receptionist.

"They need some behavior modification," I said.

JC and I watched as the receptionist headed back to her window shaking her head in wonderment.

Smiling broadly, JC said, "You are a tormentor of animals and old ladies. There is a dark side to you, Mike."

"Her and her dog deserved it. How are you feeling?" I asked.

"I'm beginning to climb the walls staying home," JC said. "I gotta get out of the house soon or I'll go stark raving nuts."

"I thought I was better but I felt weak this morning at breakfast. I don't think I'm well enough to go back to work, yet," I said.

"I think that I would rather go back on light duty then be stuck in the house all day. I'm starting to know all the soap stars by name and I'm yelling at the TV," JC laughed.

"Mr. Colby," the nurse called. "You're next."

The doctor put JC back to light duty for a few weeks like JC wanted, and he told me I still had some infection near the stitches. He gave me more antibiotics and sent me home for another week.

"You need a ride, JC?" I asked.

"Yeah, that would be great," JC said.

The traffic was mild in Upper Manhattan that time of the morning and in no time at all we were heading over the 59th Street bridge into Queens.

"Are you going home?" I asked.

"No. Just drop me off at Finty's pub in Astoria, I think I'll have one of those huge hamburgers and a few beers. Care to join me?" JC asked.

"That sounds good. Just point me in the right direction."

Finty's was an old neighborhood bar on the edge of the Woodside and Astoria borders. Only characters frequented bars at eleven in the morning and this place was crawling with them. We walked past one old-timer who stood in the middle of the floor in a boxer's stance, mumbling like a sports announcer and jabbing at the air.

"Mickey Cochran, Harry Greb, and the toy bulldog will fight to the death," the old-timer said.

"Sit yourself down now and don't be bothering these people," the bartender said, pointing at the old boxer.

"Is that a relative?" JC jokingly asked the bartender.

"It could very well be. On my wife's side of the family, of course," the bartender laughed. "What can I get you boys?"

"Mike, this ugly Irishman behind the bar is Paddy Finty, the proprietor of this hellhole."

Holding out my hand, I said, "Nice to meet you, Paddy."

"Likewise, Michael, although if you're a friend of this slug, I might regret our meeting," said Finty with just a hint of his Irish brogue.

"We'll take two of your deluxe burgers and two mugs of Budweiser," said JC.

"You dining at the bar?" asked Finty.

"No. We'll take our order in the back room," said JC. "Too many of your relatives are acting up today."

We ate our lunch and drank our beer without saying too much, only once in a while commenting on the afternoon news on television.

"That hamburger sure was man-size, JC," I said.

"Yeah, it fills up the old gut," JC said. "Want another beer?" JC asked.

"No. Two is my limit," I said.

After getting another beer from the bar JC sat down across from me, took a sip of his drink, and said, "What happens now, Mike?"

"You drink up and we go home. What do you think happens now?" I said.

"I mean about the case we're working on. What's next?" JC asked.

"Oh, that," I said. "I have been trying to put it out of my mind since I got shot."

"I bet you dollars to donuts the brains behind Oliveri didn't put it out of their minds!" JC said.

I didn't answer him right away but looked at my glass on the table as I slowly turned it in small circles, reliving the night in the alley.

JC began knocking his fist on my head saying, "Hello. Anybody at home in there?"

"I've done nothing but think since that night," I said as I leaned back in the chair.

"Yeah, so what then?" JC said.

"Did you get a look at any of that stuff in the locker? You know, the one at Grand Central Station?" I asked.

"No. IAD has that stuff in the property clerk's office. Why?"

"I don't know, but unless we come up with something, this case will end with Oliveri," I said. "Can you get me a list of items that came from that locker?"

JC stared at me with a faraway look in his eye and said, "Yeah, sure I can. Me and IAD are tight as identical twins," JC joked. "I'll call Captain Sylvester right now and pick up a copy of the voucher this afternoon."

Pushing the beer to the center of the table, I stood up and patted JC on the shoulder and said "After you get a copy, stop by the house and we'll have lunch tomorrow. Karen and the baby will be at her mother's, so we can talk."

"I'll call when I get it," JC said. "Safe drive home."

When Karen came home I was asleep on the couch in the living room.

"Wake up, sleepy head!" Karen said while poking me in the arm.

Sleepily I pushed myself up on one elbow and asked, "What time is it? I didn't mean to fall asleep."

"It's six o'clock and time for dinner, " Karen said. "How does a thick sirloin steak sound?"

"Great! I'm starving," I said.

"How did it go at the doctor's today?" Karen asked.

"He gave me more antibiotics and said one more week at home," I said.

Karen's silence to what I had said spoke volumes about the way she was feeling. She was worried but reluctant to add her worries to mine. Still waters run deep, and in Karen's case her emotions were buried in chasms.

The following morning JC was at my house bright and early. He brought the property clerk vouchers and two large bacon and egg hero sandwiches.

"Are we gonna eat that or sail on it?" I asked.

"A good breakfast starts the day off right, Mike," JC said.

While JC was tearing apart his hero, I tried to see if there was anything we missed listed in the property.

"You know these pictures don't show the boss man's face," I said.

"Yeah, they were good burglars but lousy photographers," JC said.

"We screwed up," I said. "We managed to get two people killed and left a woman and her children on poverty row."

"Quit beating yourself up over this. Oliveri murdered those two burglars, not us. Sooner or later that woman would've ended up alone anyway, considering what her husband and brother did for a living," JC said. "Besides, she's doing better financially now than she ever did before, what with Social Security for widows and dependent children."

With my arms folded across my chest, I struck a defiant pose and said, "I don't want to see anybody else get hurt."

"Sometimes, getting shot can make you gun shy. It's understandable," JC said.

"This isn't about me! It's about us trying to be detectives and people dying because we got in over our heads," I said.

Slowly, JC got up from the kitchen table, walked over to the coffee pot, and poured another cup of coffee.

"If we don't see this to the end, those men will have died for nothing," JC said. "Is that what you want?"

"I don't know what else to do. Without a lead, or a witness, the case is dead," I said.

"It's just not right letting the brains behind Oliveri get away with murder," JC said.

"There's no statute of limitations on murder. Something will break, I'm sure of it," I said.

"Don't hold your breath," JC said.

As we sat at the table staring at our coffee cups, the phone rang, and it was Captain Mendolsohn, our precinct commanding officer.

"Yes, Captain. No, I'm feeling fine. Thanks for asking," I said. "What's up?" After I got off the phone with Mendolsohn, I looked at JC and said, "You won't believe what he just said."

"What? Are we going to jail?" JC asked.

"Friday, at police headquarters, we are being promoted to Third Grade Detective. Can you believe it!" I said.

The two of us sat staring at each other, dumbfounded by the news, unable to celebrate or explain what we were feeling.

CHAPTER *18*

ENRIQUE TOUSSANT HAD IMMIGRATED TO New York three years ago and was attending City College at night while working twelve hours a day at the Stagger Inn bar and grill on 14th Street and 4th Avenue. He wasn't allowed to tend bar, but he did every other job they had, from dishwasher to making the bank drop, like he was preparing to do tonight. Enrique was double-checking the deposit slip on the bar when he heard a crash of bottles in the storeroom.

"Is that you, Boots? You're too old and fat to catch those mice," Enrique called out. Walking toward the storeroom, Enrique called out once more. "Boots, is that you?" The butt of a shotgun smashed into Enrique's mouth, knocking his front teeth onto the barroom floor. "Oh, my God!" Enrique moaned while rolling in pain on the floor.

"Go check the bar out," ordered the short, muscular leader of the robbery crew. "Watch out that no passing pigs spot you."

The tall, thin robber raced behind the bar and quickly grabbed the weekend receipts. Without bothering to count it, he shoved the bills into his coat pocket and said, "I got the green, man. Cap the hashhead and let's book."

While Enrique writhed in pain on the floor, the leader of the crew grabbed his shoulder and turned him onto his back. Shoving his shotgun under Enrique's chin, the leader said, "I'm the last fuckin' thing you will ever see in this lousy world, man." *BOOM.* The shotgun roared and most of Enrique's head splattered on the wall and mirror. "Oh, man! Did you see the awesome power of this gun?" said the leader.

The three robbers rushed into the waiting car in the alley behind the bar and slowly pulled away.

Captain Stanley and Sergeant Jimmy Ahearn stood silently over the body of Enrique Toussant and seemed to be in deep thought. Stanley clenched his teeth and spoke loudly, but in measured sequence.

"We've got to nail these humps before any more poor bastards get killed!"

"These scumbags are sick," Sergeant Ahearn said.

"The crew that is doing this is not sick, they are evil. Being sick is a condition or disease. Evil is behavior, a choice. Sickness is something that happens. Evil is inflicted. People are not what they think they are—they are what they do. Sickness should be treated, and evil should be fought," Captain Stanley said.

Looking intently at the captain, Sergeant Ahearn asked, "Are there any further orders, boss?

"I want an emergency meeting in the borough HQ at ten a.m. tomorrow with all the whips of the Manhattan North detective squads. No exceptions!" Captain Stanley ordered. "Have the CO of the stakeout unit there as well."

As Sergeant Ahearn turned to leave, the captain waved to the two precinct cops who had the sector that covered the crime scene.

"Yes, sir, Captain?" Patrolman Kimler said.

"I am about to give you the lousiest job there is to give, Officer. You and your partner will have to go tell the wife of the victim that her husband won't be coming home tonight...or any other night. Try to be as sensitive as you can without saying too much. Words fall on deaf ears at a time like this. If there is anything the department can do for her, call me direct," Captain Stanley said. "Notify me when the notification is made."

The two officers moved reluctantly to their radio car and informed the central dispatcher they were out of service with a notification.

Captain Stanley stood for a long time watching the crime scene unit go through their paces. He was contemplating the strategy he was going to use and what tools he would need.

"All notifications have been made, Captain. Anything else?" Sergeant Ahearn asked.

"Get me a list of cops in my borough that have been involved in shootouts, or recent combat veterans. Get it to me at tomorrow's meeting," Captain Stanley ordered.

CHAPTER 19

I WAS SURPRISED TO SEE so few people at police headquarters for the promotion ceremony, but my wife thought it was cozy, and these promotions were considered "on the spot" and weren't planned like the hundreds that take place on a regular schedule. Mayor Warren officiated, and his speech was mostly positive, although he did reference the wildcat police strike that was held recently.

"Police officers have a special calling and are our first line of defense, who put aside their personal feelings and continue to protect and serve the public," Warren said.

"If we're so special, then where is our raise. It's been six years since our last contract," JC said.

"Sshh," admonished my wife. "I want to hear this."

JC and I were both laughing nervously again at my wife's rebuke.

"I feel like I'm back at Our Lady of the Miraculous Medal," JC said while giggling.

They called our names, gave us our new detective shields, and shook our hands. Just like that we were part of the "squad" and JC was already calling every cop "kid."

"Number 351. That's an old number, isn't it, JC?" I asked.

"Yeah, my number is 3082. Yours might have some history behind it, while I'm going to make some history of my own," JC said.

The chief of detectives, Clive Little, stepped onto the platform and said, "I have an announcement. The following men will report to Rodman's Neck in the Bronx tomorrow morning... Detective James Colby and Detective Michael Halley. Bring soft clothes and all your weapons, and report to Sergeant Sean O'Sullivan for training. That's all. DISMISSED."

As we left the auditorium, I asked JC, "Why only you and me? Everybody else got three days off before any new assignment."

"Whatever it is, it's a rush job," JC said. "Besides, at least they didn't tell us to go to typing class, so we know we are still street cops."

"And that's a good thing?" I said.

After showing our shield and ID card at the security booth at Rodman's Neck, JC and I pulled into the parking lot near the "Welcome to City Island" sign. The breeze from the ocean was cool and salty.

"I love this place, man," said JC. "It's hard to believe that City Island is part of the Bronx."

"Ssshhh…If the city of New York hears you, they'll sell the island to land developers for condominiums," I said. "Come on, let's get coffee and check in."

After getting a roll and some coffee we sat at a table in the mess hall and watched other cops and detectives checking in with the range officers. Each cop presented all the guns he owned to be recorded and inspected for imperfections.

"Your 10 card says you own a derringer. Where is it?" Sergeant Sullivan asked.

"I sold that six months ago to a dealer, but don't have the paperwork on it?" Detective Zack said.

"You have thirty days to get the transaction record up to date or face disciplinary charges," Sergeant O'Sullivan said.

"Okay, sure," Detective Zack said.

Opening the chamber of Zack's off-duty Colt and holding the weapon away from himself, Sergeant O' Sullivan began pulling out a piece of impacted material stuck in the barrel.

"What the hell is this?" Sergeant O'Sullivan said while holding it aloft for the entertainment of the entire mess hall. "Some kind of new bullet."

Detective Zack's face turned beet red as he hemmed and hawed trying to explain how a piece of pizza crust got into the cylinder of his gun.

"I have no idea how that got in there! I take care of my guns!" Zack said while trying to avoid the stares and the laughter.

"It's a good thing it wasn't pepperoni, cause that can cause blindness if fired at close range," Sergeant O'Sullivan joked. As the laughter died down O'Sullivan stood up and said, "It would be wise to check your guns every once in a while, to make sure they are in good working condition. Who knows, it might even save your life someday."

There were only five of us assigned to the same room, and as we sat down, Sergeant O'Sullivan introduced himself to us.

"I am Sergeant Sean O'Sullivan and I will be your firearms instructor for the next five days. You will be trained in the use of five different weapons and you will become proficient enough to qualify on delta range. Any questions?" O'Sullivan asked. The sergeant was a tall, square-jawed Irishman who looked every bit the man in charge.

JC leaned over toward me and whispered, "If you don't qualify, O'Sullivan will kick your ass."

"Before we start the training, I would like to introduce Captain Stanley of the Manhattan robbery squad who has a few words to say," Sergeant O'Sullivan said.

Captain Stanley entered the room dressed in a suit and tie and carrying a leather briefcase.

"Good morning, men. The reason you're here on such short notice is because of the assignment you have and the urgency of that assignment. There is a robbery team of four men who have killed eleven men and one woman in cold blood. With your help, I aim to put a stop to these bastards."

Going through his briefcase, Stanley pulled out a handful of papers and handed them to all of us in the room. Looking through them, I could see that this case unnerved the captain enough for him to pull out all the stops.

"As you can see by the photos of the victims, the shootings were executions. I chose you men because you have had experience either with firefights while a member of the department or as a soldier in combat. The felons we are hunting won't be brought back alive. So, with that knowledge, I want to make it clear that this detail is strictly voluntary. Anyone who would rather be reassigned, please let me know now. There will be no hard feelings."

No one in the room moved a muscle. Everybody kept staring at the graphic forensic pictures of the crime scenes.

"Thank you. This assignment is not good duty, but it must be done. I look forward to seeing you all out on the street. Good luck, men," said Stanley.

CHAPTER 20

THE FIVE DAYS I SPENT at the range was the most enjoyable time I had spent in the department and the time seemed to fly by. Both JC and I qualified on all the weapons we were given, but I fell in love with a plain .22 caliber rifle with a high-powered exploding shell. After hitting its mark, the bullet would explode on contact. The idea was to stop anyone they were shot at. These guns were meant to kill as quickly as possible with as little risk of return fire as could be managed. The words "deadly murderers" were used all week to describe the stick-up teams we were looking for. Two words that were never mentioned were "arrest or capture." All of us at that range knew the gravity of our assignment and the people we were up against.

During the next week we were sent through a tactical course designed strictly for the stakeout unit. The course consisted of us entering stores where a robbery was in progress or secreting ourselves in the rear of a store and taking action when a stickup was announced. With so much firepower involved we had to be trained not to get caught in a crossfire, or worse, have a cop or bystander killed by friendly fire. We all made some blunders, but all in all these men had been in shootouts before and they got the hang of it very fast. After watching these men in action, I thought the edge was definitely on our side. Of course, nobody was shooting real bullets at us, so only time would tell. The difference between my training in the army and the police department was the department worried about collateral damage more than the American government. The city could be sued for any mistakes made by its police force while the government was not an easy target for lawsuits. Their aims were different as well—crime versus war. In war you pull out all stops, while crime should be fought with a scalpel. In this upcoming battle, though, the robbery squad was getting ready for war.

While we trained to face one group of murderers, another group was becoming very active in our old precinct. It was around 2000 hours when two rookie cops met for supper on Avenue B and 10th Street, Greg Booker and Angelo Laurenti, fresh out of the academy and friends since day one. Booker, a tall black man from Harlem, and Laurenti, a short muscular Italian from Sicily, met every chance they got for a shared meal period. As they hurried toward a local diner laughing and joking, they were oblivious to the three men that followed close behind. Both men were still laughing as the bullets crashed into Laurenti's back and Booker's head, sending the cops sprawling to the sidewalk. An eyewitness later told police that Booker was still alive when one of the shooters knelt down near his face and shot his eyes out.

"That's a lesson for you fucking Uncle Toms," the assassin yelled at the mutilated cop.

"Power to the people," the other two killers yelled in unison while holding their clenched fists in the air.

Most cops on the scene were very upset and confused by the seemingly random act of murder of two rookie cops.

"Why did they shoot these poor bastards?" asked Sergeant Boyle rhetorically. "They hadn't even written a parking ticket yet."

Also, on the scene was Deputy Commissioner John Bailey, an ex-newspaperman who said to Sergeant Boyle, "Let's not be in a rush to make martyrs out of these two men. This has all the earmarking's of a mob hit. Maybe a drug deal gone bad."

"Who the fuck are you to disparage these two men when you don't know your ass from your elbow about them!" yelled Sean Kilcommons, a Patrolmen's Benevolent delegate. Two cops and the sergeant held Kilcommons back from attacking Bailey.

"Who is that man?" demanded Bailey.

"I'll rip your stinkin' throat out you liberal no-nothing lackey," screamed Kilcommons.

Two unidentified cops dragged the delegate away and drove off down Avenue B. "I want that insubordinate cop's name," demanded Bailey.

"As a newspaper man you should know better than to make an assumption like the one you made tonight as a deputy commissioner in the police department. What you said was not only unprofessional but was an insult to the men and women in this job. I can't order you to leave the scene, but I think you have become a distraction to the investigation and I am respectfully requesting you leave," said Sergeant Boyle.

Bailey seemed stunned by the sergeant's word. Backing toward his car, he looked at the sergeant and said, "This is probably the end of your career, Sergeant," Bailey said while pointing a finger at him.

"I have two dead cops and you wanna get into a pissing contest! FINE! See you in the trial room, Commissioner. Now hit the road," said Boyle.

The irony about that night was the commissioner never did bring charges against anybody, but instead wrote a best-selling novel about his short stint in the department. In his book this incident, the first of several "Black Liberation Army" assassinations, was written entirely differently than witnesses remember. As I remember in the retelling of the story, the remark was attributed to some superior officer on the scene who remained nameless. Sergeant Boyle's name was never mentioned.

CHAPTER *21*

OUR FINAL DAY AT THE range was mostly about being issued our Kevlar vests and getting our assignments from Sergeant Ahearns of the Manhattan South robbery squad. JC and I were both assigned to Stakeout Unit 4 to 12 tour. We were given three days off before reporting for duty in the basement of the old 5ᵗʰ Precinct station house.

"Have any plans for your time off, JC?" I asked.

"Yeah. My son and I are going to the Bronx Zoo and the Museum of Natural History for the day," JC said.

"Well, that sounds great. Have a good time and I'll see you Wednesday at the 9," I said.

"Yeah...don't forget your vest. We're gonna need it," JC snickered.

The drive to Long Island took only forty minutes from City Island and I thought how nice it had been these past couple of weeks at the range. I had envied Sergeant O'Sullivan and all the members of the Firearms Unit for their dedication to the job, and most of all, to their great assignment. I thought that someday I'd like to teach at City Island.

Pulling into the driveway, Karen came running out the door with a worried look on her face.

"What's wrong?" I asked. "Is it Annie?"

"No, Michael. It's your dad. He had a heart attack and is at Smithtown General with your mother," Karen said. "I think you better go right away."

"Is he in ICU, a room, what?" I asked.

"The emergency room," Karen yelled as I sped back down the driveway into the street.

As I watched my father lying in bed, part man, part machine, it became apparent to me that he was actually dying, his sharp eyes and inquisitive mind blunted by his failing heart and diminished oxygen to the brain.

"How could this be?" I asked my mother. "Weren't there any warning signs?"

"If there were, he never said anything," said my mother, Pat Halley.

"Don't you remember when your father was in a car accident with his brother John and his wife Olga on Queens Boulevard a few years back? Your father drove them both to St. John's Hospital for treatment while he waited in the emergency room with a broken collar bone."

"He should have said something," I said.

"You know he didn't want to worry us," said my mother.

What I was really trying to say was why didn't he confide in me? After all, I was a family man myself, a war veteran, a cop. Hell, if I couldn't deal with bad news, nobody could. I stood there in the hospital room shuffling my feet and trying like hell to hold back the tears. There was so much I wanted to tell my dad, so much left unsaid. That night, Michael Anthony Halley passed away in his sleep. He never regained consciousness. I was the basket case in the family and my mother was the strong one.

The wake was held at Phillip's Funeral Home in Maspeth, Queens, the following morning. Most of my father's friends and relatives were dead, but all those who still had breath attended the wake. The wake was only one day with the burial at Pinelawn Cemetery the following morning. My father's brother-in-law, Murray Cohen, wanted to say a few words at the late-night invocation. He wished to say the prayer of the Kaddish—the Jewish prayer of the dead.

"Is it all right if I say this prayer for Mike, Pat?" Murray asked my mother. "We need a minyan, a group of ten or more."

"We all pray to the same God, Murray. Of course, it's all right," said my mother.

Murray walked to the front of the room, bowed his head, and said, "Please join me as I say the prayer for the dead." Holding his hands outstretched, Murray said, "Magnificent and sanctified be his great name, throughout the world, which he created according to his will. May God be blessed, praised, extolled, honored, glorified and exalted. Amen." Murray walked over to my mother, took her hand, and said, "Mike is home now, Pat. His race is run."

On hearing this, my mother began to quietly sob, the first real emotion she showed since my father's death.

The following day my father received a full military funeral with taps, rifle salute, and flag-folding ceremony. After the soldiers moved away, Father Gregory of Good Shepherd parish stepped forward to lead the mourners in prayer.

"In life, whenever we lose something that we love, we try to find it with our whole being. If we fail to find it, we fall back on hope and say it'll turn up. But when that loss is the death of a loved one, our loss is permanent, heartfelt, and devastating. But with the help of God, hope springs eternal in that we shall all be reunited in Christ in the house that our Lord has prepared for us. May the soul of Michael Halley, and all the souls of the faithfully departed, rest in peace. Amen," he said.

My mother had everybody back to my aunt's house in Middle Village, Queens. JC and a couple of cops from the precinct were at the cemetery and returned to my aunt's later.

Father Gregory was talking to JC and Arthur Comize when he asked if they had heard the joke about the dead jackass. When they both shook their head no, Father Gregory began the joke with his best Irish brogue.

"Father O'Malley got up one fine spring day and walked to the window of his bedroom to get a deep breath of the beautiful day outside and noticed there was a jackass lying dead in the middle of his front lawn. He promptly called the local police station. The conversation went like this:

"'Top of the morning to ye. This is Sergeant Flaherty. How may I help you?'

"'And the rest of the day te yeself. This is Father O'Malley at St Brigid's. There's a jackass lying dead in me front lawn. Would ye be after sending a couple o' yer lads to take care of the matter?'

"Sergent Flaherty considered himself to be quite a wit and the rest of the conversation proceeded.

"'Well now, Father, it was always me impression that ye people took care o' last rites!'

"There was dead silence on the line for a moment and then Father O'Malley replied, 'Aye, tis certainly true, but we are also obliged to notify next of kin,' Gregory said."

JC enjoyed the joke the most, rolling with laughter, while Comize politely laughed at the Irish humor.

"Well, on that note I believe I'll be running along, Michael. You keep an eye on your mother. She's all alone now for the first time in forty years. She is gonna need you more than ever," Father Gregory said. "If you or your mother need my help, don't hesitate to call."

Slipping a fifty into his hand I said, "Thank you, Father, I appreciate your being here."

After everyone had left, I sat in the living room with Karen watching the late news on television.

"You know, Michael, we have plenty of room at our house. Maybe it might be a good idea if your mother stayed with us for a while," Karen said.

"That's a good idea, Karen. I'll ask her in the morning," I said. "Tonight, she needs to be alone."

"You didn't know my father very well, did you, Karen?" I asked.

"No, we only met a couple of times and he seemed preoccupied. But he did talk to me on our wedding day," Karen said.

"Really? About what?" I asked.

"He said to keep an eye on you, and when I laughed, he said he wasn't joking. He went on to say that you were compulsive just like him and you needed someone strong to anchor you to the realities of life. At the time, I didn't understand what he was talking about, but I do now," Karen said.

"Oh really! He said that?" I asked. "I asked Mom why she didn't pick up on any early warning signs about his illness, but I've been sitting here remembering the last time we got together and something that he said that bothered me," I said.

"What was that?" asked Karen.

"At Annie's birthday party when we were saying goodbye at the door. He usually said things like take care of yourself or catch you later, but this time was different. He said good-bye, son, I love you. A strange feeling came over me that night and stayed with me all the way home. I told myself he was indestructible, and I was just being maudlin. I missed the sign, Karen," I said.

"Even if you confronted him with it, you know he would have made light of it and nothing would have been done. You couldn't have saved him, Michael," Karen said.

The tears began to rush down my face as I tried to make sense of death. Karen held out her arms to me and I held her tight while all my emotions burst through.

"I never realized how much I had looked up to him and tried to emulate him in all things. Like the old song goes, he taught me things not known to kings, and I miss him," I said through the tears.

CHAPTER 22

THREE MONTHS HAD PASSED SINCE my father's funeral and JC and I had been on stakeout duty the whole time and we hadn't seen squat.

"If I had known I would have so much free time, I would have read Tolstoy's *War and Peace*," JC said.

"You probably would be finished by now," I said.

"I didn't know you could read, Colby," said Bob Stamos.

"Very funny, you freakin' penguin," said JC.

Stamos was a short, muscular cop who teetered from side to side when he walked, looking just like a penguin. Only JC would have dared call Stamos a penguin because Stamos was a loose cannon with a hair-trigger temper. Outside the range, Stamos was the best shot in the department. Looking at JC, Stamos smiled and said, "Someday you might catch a ricochet, Colby."

"You're too good a shot to convince a jury you messed up," JC said.

Stamos had been in the stakeout unit for two years and had been involved in three firefights with three confirmed kills.

"What do you think, Betsy? Should we shoot old Colby or not?" Stamos said to his service weapon.

I watched JC point at Stamos and whisper, "I told you so."

He was referring to the night he warned me about volunteering for this unit, and how I refused to believe that men in this outfit had names for their guns.

"Does Betsy ever answer you, Stamos?" JC joked.

With a strange look in his eye Stamos looked at his gun and said, "When Betsy talks, people die."

Although it was quiet for us, other cops weren't so lucky.

It was 1900 hours on Friday in the 113th Precinct in Jamaica, Queens, and Officers Jim Resnick and Mike O'Hara had been ordered to pick up their summons activity. It was the end of the month and both officers were last again in their squad. Both officers watched as a white van made a right turn on a red light.

"There's a mover, Jimmy."

Let's pull him over," Mike O"Hara said.

Resnick put on the red turret light and touched the siren a couple of times until the van pulled to the side of the road. The rear doors of the van opened, and shots began hitting the windshield of the radio car. Both cops yelled in pain as bullets began ripping into their flesh.

Fumbling for his gun between the door and the passenger seat, O'Hara watched as a black female walked casually to his side of the car, poked her nine-millimeter through the window, and fired two more rounds into Resnick. *Click…click…click* the gun sounded. Both shooters ran back to the van, stepped through the rear doors, and sped away.

"Ten-thirteen! Ten-thirteen!" O'Hara screamed into the radio. "Two officers shot, 103rd Avenue and 112th Street."

Reaching across the seat, O'Hara pulled Resnick's head from the steering wheel and tried to feel a pulse in his neck. Resnick was still alive, but unconscious. O'Hara looked down on the floor of the car and his shoes were under a pool of blood. O'Hara began feeling lightheaded and began transmitting a description of the van and its occupants over the radio.

"All units, description of escaped felons are one male black accompanied by a black female, armed with nine millimeter automatics. Escaped in a white van. Partial plate number is New York 8072. Last seen heading east toward Grand Cent…"

O'Hara passed out before he could complete his transmission, but both officers survived. The newspaper headlines screamed, "Two Cops Ambushed in Queens—Mayor Vows Justice. "

Spokesmen for the FBI said they were working with local law enforcement to capture these assassins and were following all leads. Task force hotlines were set up, and for the first time in recent memory, the FBI actually had a vested interest in helping cops with crime. The director of the FBI said, "This is a war of good and evil, and we can't afford to lose."

The reaction in local police stations throughout the city was negative, the idea that a black group of radicals believed that shooting cops would push their agenda for a nondiscriminatory government made no sense. The shootings also made it personal. Guns were drawn on every car stop, and the police unions were demanding high-powered weapons and shotguns in every car. The policy to yell out, "Police, freeze!" before firing weapons was now ridiculed in police circles. The attacks on police as the enforcers of unjust laws just hardened the resolve of law and order candidates to dump liberal politicians and take our streets back from the punks. Charles Bronson starred in a very successful movie that year called *Vigilante*. The pendulum of public opinion was beginning to swing back toward less liberal thinking and to a society that enforces its laws. Unfortunately, the spawn of the times was still operating, and until it was eliminated, the streets of New York were still far from safe. The stakeout unit was a tool constructed to battle the dregs our society had reared. Sometimes it was a devastating tool.

It was cold and raining in the 13th Precinct at about 2330 hours on Saturday. The drugstore owner was counting his receipts for the day when two men opened the front door and quickly moved to the counter.

"Got any Trojans, doc?" asked the short, nervous junkie.

"Sure, the bottom shelf has all you want," said Mel Kaufman, owner of the Midway Pharmacy.

Pulling a small silver-plated revolver from under his shirt, the gunman said, "Give us all your damn money or you're a dead man."

Opening the register, Kaufman said, "It's all yours."

As had been prearranged, Kaufman dropped to the floor behind the counter, and as the gunman stared in disbelief, a withering stream of bullets smashed into both stickup men as their bodies were pushed across the entire store by the force of the high-powered guns. The noise level of all those guns going off in such confined conditions left me and JC temporarily deaf.

"I told you guys to wear your earplugs. Maybe next time you'll listen," said Stamos as he pushed the lifeless body of the gunman nearest the door.

"Oh...MY GOD!" yelled Mel Kaufinan. "They are both dead!"

"What the hell did you expect?" said Stamos.

Pulling JC and me aside out of earshot of the store owner, Stamos asked us, "Did you both get off shots?"

"No. I thought you were supposed to ask him to surrender or freeze or something other than to shoot right off the bat," I said.

"You thought wrong, Halley. When the boss gets here you tell him and Internal Affairs that you didn't fire for fear of hitting Kaufman from your angle," Stamos said. "There is nothing in the penal law that says we are required to warn armed felons of their impending demise."

Standing in the middle of the store, among the carnage, I understood only too clearly our mission in the unit. What General Patton told his men before going into battle with the German army came to mind. He said he didn't want American soldiers to die for their country. Instead, he wanted them to kill the enemy. Make the bastards die for their country. Today we made the bastards die for our country and I didn't feel good about it at all. Not at all.

The *Daily News* carried a short write-up about the stickup on the obituary page and no mention of our names in the column.

"What do you think of that, Karen? Two men dead and reporters leave out the names of the shooters. I wonder what the department promised to keep our unit a secret," I said.

"Why is your unit a secret?" Karen asked.

"Captain Stanley wants to nail a certain bunch and doesn't want to tip them off before we get a crack at them. At least that's my guess," I said.

"You don't sound convinced, Michael. What else could it be?" Karen asked.

Shrugging my shoulders, I continued to read the sports column, but her question kept nagging at the back of my mind. The answer to her question might be that what we're doing could be a tad illegal, not to mention the morality of the situation. I just didn't feel comfortable doing what I was doing, and I thought I would talk it over with JC when I got back to work. On Sunday we had my mother over for dinner and we watched the *Sound of Music* on television. While we watched the set, I caught my mother crying in certain parts of the show and I was sure that it reminded her of Dad.

While driving my mother home that night, we went a long time without saying a word to one another. I was the one who finally broke the silence.

"Karen and I would love for you to come live with us, Mom," I blurted out.

"Really? Well, that is awful sweet of Karen, but I have lived in my old house for forty years now and the memories are all I have left of your father, Michael. I'm not ready to give them up yet," Mom said.

"Living in that big house all alone on a dead-end street isn't very safe, Mom," I said. "Not to mention the financial rewards if you moved closer to me and Karen."

"I appreciate the offer, Michael, but I'm not ready to move just yet. But you tell Karen that I love her for thinking of me. Please, don't worry about me. I'll be fine," Mom said.

I didn't know what else to say to my own mother about taking care of her, so I sat in the car like a mute chauffeur all the way home. We said our good-byes in her kitchen and I headed back to the Island. When I told Karen what my mother had said, she raised her eyebrows and said, "It wasn't the right time. We'll ask again after a while."

The way she took the news seemed to make me feel better about the way my mother reacted to my question. I thought it was some woman thing and that mom would come around if given time.

"Next time, I would like you to ask Mom if you don't mind, Karen," I said. "Maybe you can penetrate the female mystique for me and get her to change her mind."

"Okay, Michael. Next time I 'll ask her," Karen said. "Stop fretting about it now. Everything will be fine. You'll see."

CHAPTER 23

THE NEXT DAY I MET JC and some of the precinct gang for a round of golf at Rock Hill Country Club near Middle Island. JC and I edged out Tony Balboni and his partner Dale Hunnicut, two real nice uniform cops from the 11th Precinct.

"We shouldn't have to buy drinks for you, JC, when you cheat so much," Tony said.

Tony took life and everything in it seriously, and JC didn't. The two were like oil and water, but Hunnicut and me kept them away from each other.

"God, you know you apple up every time we play you, Baloney, and it hurts taking your money,"

JC said.

"First off, it's Balboni not Baloney, wiseass, and you have never beaten us fair and square," Balboni said.

"As long as I'm drinking on your dime, you word it any way that makes you happy, Bratwurst," JC said.

Balboni began moving toward JC, and Hunnicut stepped between the two of them and said, "Come on, guys, let's grow up a little now. It was only a game and buying beer for Colby just brings him closer to the "farm," Hunnicut said.

The farm was the word used by cops to refer to the place in upstate New York where it was rumored that a squad of big, burly cops would grab drunken cops and whisk them away for treatment. The place was run by Father John Devlin, chaplain and Holy Name priest of the police department. Father Devlin could make or break a career in the department, and he seemed to revel in his position.

"Speaking of the farm, Gallagher came back yesterday all bright and shiny like a brand-new penny," Hunnicut said.

"He went to the farm?" I asked.

"Yeah. They said his wife turned him in and he was gone over eight weeks," Hunnicut said.

"That ain't cheap up there, either." Balboni said.

Gallagher told us the story of how after a few days of detox he went to talk to Devlin in his office. Devlin asked him if he was a hunter and Gallagher said he only shot small game when he was a kid but didn't like deer hunting and such. Looking straight into Gallagher's soul, Father Devlin said, "Have you ever hunted for your car after a night of binge drinking?"

Gallagher nodded his head up and down while looking at the floor.

"If I were to put a glass of whiskey on this desk right now, what would you do with it?" Devlin asked.

"Either fuck it or drink it. Either one will do," Gallagher said.

"That's why he spent the extra four weeks, I guess," said Hunnicut.

"He's a pisser that Gallagher," said JC laughing.

We stayed late at the golf course and had dinner. JC brought a woman to the table named Lisa and was trying to score, but she only had eyes for Balboni. While JC was talking to her, she had her foot up Balboni's pant leg, a secret shared by everyone at the table except JC.

"So, what do you boys do for a living?" Lisa asked.

"I'm in construction," Balboni lied.

Reaching over, Lisa felt Balboni's muscle. "I can see that, Tony," Lisa gushed.

Steam was beginning to come out of JC's ears as he watched the not so veiled come-on.

"Are you all construction workers?" Lisa asked.

We all nodded yes and continued the deception. Most cops feel it's better to keep quiet about being cops, as the job always seems to get in the way of conversation. All the "I got a summons once" and "Should you cops drink and drive" rhetoric can sometimes turn confrontational. Pulling a pack of tobacco paper from her pocketbook, Lisa asked us if we would like the makings.

"You guys want a hit? It's good stuff—Acapulco Gold," Lisa said.

"Mixing pot and alcohol is a good way to scramble your brain," Hunnicut said.

Getting up from the table, Lisa stumbled and grabbed onto her chair to steady herself. "I'm going to powder my nose and do a little scrambling," Lisa said laughing.

After Lisa left, JC looked around the table and said, "She's a pistol, ain't she?"

Balboni, trying to stifle a laugh, was nodding in agreement. "She gives new meaning to the word BIMBO," Balboni said.

Hunnicut and I began laughing and that seemed to infuriate JC even more. His face got beet red and he glared at Balboni and said, "What the hell would you know about women anyway, Liverwurst," JC said.

Folding his hands behind his head, Balboni leaned back in his chair and said, "I'm not the one paying alimony to a woman who cheated on me."

JC kicked his chair from under his feet and reached across the table, grabbing Balboni's shirt. Balboni slammed a left hook into JC's jaw knocking him to the floor. Hunnicut grabbed Balboni and dragged him outside for some air.

The bartender asked if I needed some help leaving. The key word was leaving.

"Sorry about this," I mumbled as I threw some money in the center of the table and began helping a sluggish JC out the door.

"Where is that big bag of shit, Balboni? I wanna thank him for ruining my night," JC said.

"Just thank your lucky stars he was sitting down when he hit you or else you'd be drinking all your meals through a straw," I said.

I locked up JC's car and put the golf clubs in my trunk. Driving JC home was mostly quiet except for the slight moans of pain when he moved his head.

"How do you feel?" I asked

"Lucky to be alive. That muscle-bound fuck can hit!" JC said while rubbing his jaw.

We both started laughing at his observation.

"I guess I have to call him tomorrow and apologize for being such a ball breaker. Hell, he was right about my ex-wife. She cheated on me from day one and I turned a blind eye to it. In some circles that makes me a cuckold, don't it, Mike?" JC asked.

"You loved and trusted her, and she let you down. If that makes you a cuckold, so be it," I said.

We didn't speak another word for the entire trip home. It was obvious that the breakup of his marriage was still bothering him and Balboni was just a convenient target to vent his frustration on. From what I had seen of divorce, it seemed that men were slower to recover from its effects than women. If anything went wrong with my marriage, I knew that I would be a basket case, not Karen. The thought of divorce was depressing, so I put it out of my mind and thought only good thoughts for the remainder of the drive.

It had been over six weeks since our golf outing and only Stakeout Unit B had seen any action. They worked Upper Manhattan and shot and killed three at a supermarket robbery on Amsterdam Avenue and 113th Street. The paper reported that "precinct detectives" stumbled onto the robbery and a gun battle

ensued, leaving three-armed robbers dead. It was further reported that the supermarket had been a robbery target six times in four months. On the same page was a story about the outrage of a coalition of minority ministers in Harlem. The headline read, "Wholesale Slaughter of Our Youth Must Stop." The thought in my mind was that no matter what cops did to protect the public, there was always someone to slap our hands for one thing or another, and a very willing press corps to print derogatory drivel. I was sure that some of these same pastors who were telling us to stop being tough on their youth were secretly hoping we would clean up Harlem and its endless cycle of crime and violence.

Our regular weekly meeting in the basement of the 5th Precinct addressed the departments concern about the body count in the units. Sergeant Aheam called the roll call and then spoke to us about police brutality complaints.

"Since the start of attacks on cops by the BLA, the department is reporting a two-hundred-percent increase in civilian complaints against the force, especially in minority communities."

"What the hell do they expect? There is a group of blacks shooting cops and they wonder why cops are a little edgy?" JC said.

Jim Brathwaite, a black detective and Vulcan delegate, disagreed. "There is a lot of truth in what those ministers said. Harlem cops act like occupational troops rather than a police force trying to help its citizens. I'm talking about white cops, of course."

Everywhere Brathwaite went he stirred the racial mix in a way that brought out the worst in everybody.

"The last time the department put a large group of black cops in Harlem precincts these same ministers begged to have them removed. It seems they beat, robbed, and fucked their way through a tour of duty," JC said.

"You're so full of shit, you honky bastard!" Brathwaite screamed.

JC stood up and went after Brathwaite, but cooler heads held the two men from getting at one another.

"AT EASE!" ordered Sergeant Ahearn. "Regardless of where the fault lies for our inability to curry favor with certain communities, we still have a job to do to stop the killings by these stickup teams and the BLA. End of story. In this job I see all of us as blue, not black or white. Anybody who has a problem with that see me after muster and I'll arrange for a transfer."

The room stayed quiet until the sergeant left, and then the men got up and moved quickly to their cars. Driving across Delancy Street onto 1st Avenue, JC was still mumbling.

"What the hell are you grumbling about?" I asked.

"That Brathwaite! He's the racist in that room, man. Did you know that the reason he was transferred to robbery from homicide is because he called his commanding officer a blue-eyed devil?" JC said.

"Yeah, he should drop the us-against-them shit and concentrate on doing his job," I said.

"What the hell does the word honky mean?" JC asked.

"I suppose any prejudiced white man," I said. "Brathwaite is a rabble-rouser, but in your case, honky might be just the right word for you."

Laughing quietly, JC turned to me and flipped me the bird and said, "Bite me, hump head."

"Are you all done with your hissy fit now?" I asked.

"You know, of the four cops killed by the BLA, two were black," JC said.

"Ahearn was right. Blue is the color of the target and Brathwaite should keep that in mind."

It was near impossible to reason with JC when he was excited and angry, so I just let him rant and rave until he ran out of gas. I kept my mouth shut throughout the ride downtown and just nodded my head whenever he asked if what he said was right!

"Are you paying attention to what I'm saying?" asked JC.

"Of course, I'm paying attention. Don't you see me trying to keep myself from falling into a coma?" I said. Looking straight ahead I avoided JC's stare until he got tired of trying to convince me to his way of thinking. Pulling to the curb at Bowery and Delancy Streets, I stepped out of the car and headed for the corner luncheonette. "You want some coffee?"

"Yeah, Light and sweet," he answered.

After getting the coffee we headed down to the old Con Edison building on 14th Street and Avenue D.

"How come you came all the way down here to have our coffee? Why not go into the place and have it? We are no longer in the bag, you know," JC said.

"You don't think people can tell we're cops with or without the uniform?" I asked.

"They can't be sure who we are. Besides, if I stay in this car too long, my suit gets all wrinkled, JC said."

"You're becoming some wussy, man," I said.

"It's time you got rid of that uniform mentality and started acting like a detective," JC said.

"Fine. This afternoon we'll have lunch at "Grady's," I replied.

"That's a gin mill, not a restaurant," JC said.

"We're in the squad now so we can have our meals in a licensed premise. After all, isn't that where the crime is?" I said.

I knew I could never win an argument with JC, but the verbal jousting made the day go by quickly. I knew once we got an assignment for a stakeout, our talking would be limited to inaudible grunts and sign language. We were both becoming very chatty in the beginning of our tours of duty.

CHAPTER 24

THE NEXT FEW WEEKS SEEM to blend into each other and I was becoming bored with all the humdrum stakeouts and uneventful patrols. Karen was after me to take some time off, so we could start fixing up the house like I had promised. Most of the inside needed a paint job and some trim needed to be replaced. To do the job right I would need a few days of uninterrupted time. The problem was that if I took off, JC would get stuck with Brathwaite as his partner.

"You stand a better chance of seeing the face of God than seeing me and Brathwaite together," JC said.

"Look, he's the odd man out in this unit and he will be teamed with whoever needs another man," I said.

"Oh sure, fuck me with a racist, commie shithead," JC said.

"Blacks can't be considered as racist because they lack the power of the white man, and sticking up for your race doesn't make you a communist. Being a shithead is something you'll have to live with. Besides, maybe the boss will have you chauffeur him," I said.

"There's a thought! Yes sir, boss. No sir, boss! All night long. Wow! I'm getting all tingly just thinking about it. Why don't I just take a sharp stick and poke it in my eye for the same effect," JC said.

"Why don't you take some vacation and give me a hand. We'll get done in half the time and we can go fishing and play golf on our time off. What do you say?" I said.

"The captain would never approve it," JC replied.

"Leave that to me. How about it?" I said.

"Anything is better than working with Brathwaite," JC said.

"I'll let you know what days we got. It'll be a blast!" I said.

"BLAST. Stop using that damn hippie lingo. You're a cop, not a flower child," JC said.

It was raining again on Friday so both golf and fishing were out.

"We should finish up the painting and trim work today, Karen. With the rain and all I don't know how to thank JC. Got any ideas?" I said.

"I could make him a nice home-cooked dinner," she replied.

"Yeah, but what about entertainment?" I said.

"Why don't you take him to that new indoor golf facility? He might enjoy it," Karen said.

"That's a great idea! Thanks, hon. You came through again," I said.

"Just make sure you're home at a reasonable hour for dinner," Karen said.

"Ain't I always?" I replied.

"No. That's why I brought it up," she said.

"Okay, okay. See you at six o' clock," I said.

The indoor golf was cheesy, but we had a lot of laughs. We seemed to be in the sand traps all day long. On a real course JC was straight as an arrow and rarely got into traps. The only way I could beat him was to take chances to cut corners, which he would never do. However, this place never gave me a chance to cut corners.

"Oh. Shit! The sand again?" I said.

"The camera doesn't like our swing, man," JC said.

"I hit that ball straight and long, but the stupid machine said I shanked it. When the hell was the last time you saw me hook a ball? Fade maybe, but shank, never." I said.

"You're just pissed because the picture says you hit like a girl," JC said.

"We'll see about that, hump. We're all even, so how about two drinks on the last hole?" I asked.

"Man, you're easy to suck into a bet. Just attack your masculinity and you're hooked. You're on," JC said.

Both of us were neck and neck until we were near the green. My chip shot was shorter than JC's but I had to shoot over a sand trap to hit the green and JC's shot was clear.

"It's your turn, JC, so don't apple up," I said.

Staring straight ahead and ignoring me altogether, JC brought the club down softly behind the ball, hitting it within a foot of the pin.

"When the going gets tough, the tough get going, JC said.

Lining up the shot I could feel JC's eyes boring through the back of my head. Just as I started to swing, JC burped, and my shot went skidding into the nearby sand trap. "God! You'd do anything to win. Balboni is right, you do cheat."

"How the hell do you think we win all the time? It ain't because of your suck-ass game that's for sure," JC said.

"Come on, let's get your ill-gotten gains before they make us drink in a sand trap," I said.

"Make way, you peasants. A champion golfer is moving to the bar," JC said.

Later that night we went home and had Karen's meatloaf, which to my surprise JC loved. We all sat around talking and watching the news on TV and JC seemed to thoroughly enjoy it.

"Thanks, Mike. I really enjoyed myself today. You've got a great family there. Don't screw it up," he said.

I watched him back out of the driveway and I was forced to agree with JC for once. I did have a great family. I thought I had a great partner, too, but I wasn't about to tell him that. His head was too big for a hat as it was.

CHAPTER 25

I ENJOYED MY TIME OFF and I got a lot done on the house so that seemed to please Karen. JC was a big help and he knew a lot about carpentry work, as it seemed his father was a master carpenter and he kept it a secret because people were always asking him for help.

"Why the hell did you become a cop with your construction skills?" I asked.

"I watched too many cowboy movies when I was a kid and I loved guns," JC chuckled.

"Still, you could start your own business if you were of a mind to," I said.

"Maybe, when I retire," JC said.

"You'll probably have arthritis of the ass by that time from sitting and drinking beer all day," I joked.

"You make that sound like a bad thing," JC said.

Karen came into the kitchen and told me that I had a phone call from the stakeout unit and they want JC and me to report to the 5th Precinct in the morning for new assignments.

"So, that's the end of our vacation to Halleyville," JC said.

"You can come to Halleyville any time you want, James," Karen said.

JC smiled and shuffled uncomfortably and said, "Thank you, Karen. I appreciate that."

"Dinner will be ready shortly so why don't you two wash up and make yourself presentable while I set the table," Karen said.

The idea of going back to work had a quieting effect on JC and me, and even Karen said little as we ate. It reminded me of the time I had R&R for a few weeks and was told I had to go back to the front lines the following morning. A quiet calm came over me then as it did now knowing it was back to the reality of what our work was all about. Bullets and evil. It was times like these that I wondered what God was up to, to allow men like the ones we chased to exist. The question would haunt me all the days of my life.

Captain Stanley stood at the platform shuffling papers while the room buzzed with everyone in the unit talking about the latest sports scores or what they did the night before.

"Attention men," Sergeant Kelly directed.

Captain Stanley handed the sergeant some composite sketches and descriptions to be handed out.

"Last night, in the confines of the 19th Precinct, our four-man stickup team struck again. This time a liquor store off 5th Avenue. As luck would have it, though, a radio car spotted their car and when they approached they got into a firefight. One cop was slightly wounded, and we believe one of the perps was also wounded leaving the store. We are passing out a description of the perps and their vehicle. Study them well," Captain Stanley admonished. "They don't seem to fear getting into it with us, so remember that if and when you come up against them."

We looked the paperwork and headed out for our assignment.

"Another liquor store?" JC whined. "Talk about closing the barn door after the horse gets out."

"Remember those two drugstores they robbed back to back?" I said. "They like to outthink us. Who knows, that may be their undoing."

"More like our undoing," JC said.

That night we got teamed up with Bob Stamos again due to the size of the liquor store and the area we had to cover.

"Oh, great. Now we get to talk to Stamos and his talking gun Betsy," JC quipped, looking at Stamos.

"Cops love it when Betsy talks cause she only hits scumbags and skells, so I would be careful JC," the Penguin said.

"How did you ever pass that psych test?" JC asked.

"Who said I passed?" Stamos said.

"Okay, ladies, let's simmer down and get ready for business," I said.

It was close to one o'clock when the front door flew open and three men rushed in.

"You, behind the counter. Step out here and be quick about it," one perp said.

"Sure, mister, whatever you say," the cashier said as he ducked behind the counter as rehearsed. "April fools, motherfucker!" screamed Stamos as Betsy spewed bullets.

The perp caught a bullet in the mouth that blew out the back of his head, and the other two were nailed by JC and me before they knew what the hell was happening. I was still trying to fire my gun when I realized it was empty. The smell of gunpowder was overwhelming, and the damage to the stickup team was sickening to see. There was blood everywhere.

"Is everybody all right?" I asked.

They all mumbled they were okay.

"Oh, my God!" exclaimed the clerk. "They are all dead."

"If we weren't here that would be you laying there," Stamos said. "Better them than you, right?"

The clerk nodded as he slumped to the floor and put his head into his hands and wept.

That night every newspaperman in the city was there, trying to talk to us as we avoided the spotlight and tried to deal with Internal Affairs and all the brass that demanded answers from us on the timeline and what each of us did and when we did it. They took our weapons for ballistics checks, and asked us if we needed to go to the hospital for evaluation for stress and we all said yes so we could get some breathing room from all the questioning.

"All I heard after he ordered me out from behind the counter while pointing his gun at me was 'April Fool, motherfucker' and shots being fired everywhere," the cashier said to our detriment.

"Who said that?" the reporters and the brass kept asking while we headed for a stress evaluation at Bellevue Hospital.

Shaking his head from side to side, JC looked at me and said, "I told you anybody that names his gun was trouble. 'April Fools, motherfucker.' Just what we needed, a calling card."

The investigation went on for days and finally the perps' guns were a match for the numerous homicides, and the newspapers began to taper off about the cavalier attitude of the stakeout unit that consisted of using men of warlike capabilities and mercenary characteristics. JC loved the description but predicted the end of the unit.

"The idea that we have a group of men who might be close to paid assassins working for the city will never be tolerated. You and I will be forever tainted with that night. If only Stamos would have kept his mouth shut none of this would have happened."

"I'm afraid you're right about this, JC. We are toast," I said. "I sure would have liked to have found out who ordered the hit on Anselmo before I was locked away in a basement," I went on.

"Maybe next time you'll listen to me and NEVER volunteer for assignments. Didn't they teach you that in the army?"

Sitting back on the gurney, I mulled over what JC said and wondered why I didn't listen to him before. Before all the shit hit the fan.

Chapter 26

KAREN AND I TOOK ANNIE to Adventureland on the Island, so we could get out of the house and away from the incessant phone calls from the press. I enjoyed watching Annie laugh and scream on the rides and seeing her face with all the cat makeup on. We took lots of pictures, and even though we were tired, we dreaded going home.

"When will this all stop, Michael?" Karen asked. "After all, they were bad people, weren't they?"

"Of course, they were. Thieves and murderers. They killed over eleven people who did no more than try to earn a living. An honest living. I hope they are in hell suffering as we speak," I said.

"Why then do the newspapers keep hounding us about doing your job?" Karen asked.

"Because a cop said something foolish, whether from fear or adrenalin, that the papers found insensitive or inappropriate. Cops are not well liked by the media or politicians right now anyway, so all the problems of the city are being dumped on us. Maybe the pendulum will swing back someday, but right now we are lepers," I said.

The ride back home was quiet, and I knew Karen was worried about the uncertainty of my job and the future. I wracked my brain trying to find the words to reassure her, but I couldn't even reassure myself, so I remained silent. Annie slept all the way home.

There were over fifty messages on the answering machine when I got home. I started the deleting process right away, but there were two messages from JC that sounded urgent, so I gave him a call.

"Hey, hump. What's up?" I said.

"Did Captain Stanley call you?" JC asked.

"I don't know. I just started deleting the answering machine when I got your message. What's going on?" I asked.

"You want the good or bad news first?" JC asked.

"There's good news?" I said.

"Well, the stakeout unit is being disbanded by order of the mayor."

"Is that the good news?" I asked

"We are getting medals at One Police Plaza Monday morning and are being reassigned," JC said.

I sat there dumbfounded, trying to process the news and make sense of it.

"Medals," I said. I began to laugh. "Medals," I repeated.

"Yeah, medals. Even that screwball Stamos and his talking gun Betsy are getting a medal. I guess they figured in the end that we only did our job, and these were the lowest form of humankind there was. Right," JC said. "So, sleep tight tonight, partner, and get ready for a new assignment Monday. Cleaning the men's room at the YMCA might not be so bad. Stamos and Betsy can be in charge of putting the blue soap in the urinals," JC said while he began to laugh.

Karen was elated when I told her the news, especially about the end of the stakeout unit and the new assignment. We took Annie to Chuckie Cheese on Sunday after Mass and the noise of screaming children was deafening. I must have been crazy to put myself through that agony, but both Annie and Karen had a ball and that's what really counts. We turned in early and slept straight through until morning. Karen's car was giving us trouble again as it was spitting and coughing and bellowing smoke, so I dropped her car at Joe's Garage and caught a cab to work. Later that day, Karen left a message that it was the carburetor and it would cost us over two hundred dollars to fix.

"Every time we get a little good news, bad news is sure to follow," I said.

"It could be worse," Karen said.

Karen used that phrase no matter the circumstance. I suppose she was the forever optimist and I was the pessimist. We were miles apart in that regard.

The medal ceremony was held in the press room of One Police Plaza and we were all awarded the Combat Cross for the fire fight we were in, even though the stickup men never fired a shot at us. The ballistic unit said that two of their weapons were fired during the shootout, probably into the walls and floor as they went down. Funny, I don't remember seeing them shoot. Too busy, I guess. We got a copy of our orders, too—assignment forthwith to Manhattan South Robbery Squad.

"A shithouse they rewarded us with," JC said. "See what a devious bunch these Irish can be, Mike."

"That's a plumb of an assignment. Easy to make Second Grade," I said.

"Easy to get jammed up, you mean," JC said.

"You should be thanking God for this chance after getting dumped once and now you have a chance at redemption and reviving your career," I said.

JC stared at me and nodded, and then said, "Murphy's Law could be at work here. Whatever can go wrong, will go wrong."

"So far we made all the right moves and luck has been with us. So, say a prayer and let's try to enjoy our success," I said.

"Yeah, sure. We'll see. We'll see," JC said.

JC called Manhattan South and the whip (squad commander) Sergeant Ahearn told us to report at 10:00 a.m. tomorrow for orientation at the Central Park Precinct, parking lot 5.

JC kept bugging me to go have a celebratory beer with him, so I finally agreed, and we stopped at Finty's for a killer hamburger and a few beers. When JC said a few beers, though, it could mean three or a few dozen, because time flies when you listen to his conspiracy theories, and after a while you begin to agree with him so that's when you know it's time to go.

"See you tomorrow, JC. Don't stay out too late or Murphy's Law will bite you in the ass with this new boss," I said.

"I'm leaving right after this beer. See you tomorrow, Mother Hubbard," JC said.

When I got home, Karen was in the living room with her mother, Ann.

"Well, hello, Ann. This is a surprise. Is Tom all right?" I asked.

"I think he is. That's why I came by to see you two," Ann said.

"What do you mean, think he is?" I said.

"Mom thinks Dad is hiding something from her and she's afraid it's his health," Karen said.

"What makes you think that?" I asked.

"There are a few things that happened recently, like doctors calling to confirm appointments and him not telling me, or asking me, to go with him. Also, the other day while he was doing some yard work I saw him trying to catch his breath and holding his chest. I'm really getting worried, Mike," Ann said.

"Why don't you ask him flat out, Ann? After all, you've been married forty years," I said.

Ann started to tear up and, reaching for a handkerchief, said, "I have asked, and he just says I'm making a mountain out of a molehill. I know he's keeping something from me and if it's bad news, I want to know about it. I think I earned the right."

"What can we do?" I asked.

"Could you talk to him? He respects you and he might confide in you," Ann said.

Looking at Karen, I shrugged my shoulders and Karen grabbed her mother's arm and said, "Of course we will, Mom. We'll figure out some ruse to see Dad and we'll see what we can do. Right, Michael? Don't you worry, Mom, we'll get some answers for you soon," Karen said while escorting her mother toward the door.

"I don't know how to thank you both. I've been besides myself with worry," Ann said. "I love you both. Goodbye."

"Well, now what?" I asked.

"My father has been after you to play golf with him for some time so now is the time," Karen said.

"I'll try for next week and bring JC. Your father thinks he's funny. Maybe I can get him to open up, but I'm not gonna force him. I'll tell him Ann came to see us and she's very worried," I said.

"Yes. Tell him his wife deserves to know what's going on, good or bad," Karen said. Looking straight at me and pointing her finger, Karen said, "You remember what I just said, mister. NO SECRETS!"

CHAPTER 27

I HAD JUST PULLED INTO parking lot 5 in Central Park when I saw JC leaning against his car drinking coffee.

"Well, partner, I told you Murphy's Law was hard at work, didn't I," JC said.

"What now?" I said.

"Guess who is also working here?" JC said.

"Who?" I said.

"Stamos and his talking gun Betsy," JC said. "How about that?"

"April Fools, motherfucker," I said laughing.

"Very funny. Those Irish are devious," JC said.

"AW, come on, give the guy a break. Think of it this way. If he weren't with us, we'd still be in the damn stakeout unit. Right?" I said.

Sergeant Aheam was in the rear office of the adjoining building near the precinct station house. We walked past a pool table with pool sticks on the wall and a dartboard next to them. Ahearn's office consisted of a small makeshift desk and two small metal chairs in front of it. JC knocked on the open door and Ahearn looked up from his desk and waved us in.

"Sergeant Ahearn, I'm John Colby and this is Mike Halley. We've been assigned here and these are our orders," JC said, placing our orders on the sergeants desk.

"Sit down, gents. I was just reading your recent exploits and I must say you guys have been up to your eyeballs in shootouts. Did you know most cops do twenty years and never fire their gun? You men sure have screwed up that statistic. Right?" Ahearn said while staring right at us without cracking a smile.

"Just lucky, I guess," JC said.

"Well, welcome aboard," Ahearn said while holding his hand out to shake. "For your first week here I'm going to school you on how I want the 61s and the unusuals written and what kind of cases we need to close down here as opposed to Manhattan North, which has more of a political bent to their dealings with the public than we have. Our borough commander Inspector Joe Breen wants to be notified immediately if there is any case that might have public interest. Any questions?"

"What kind of tours will we be working, and do we work in pairs or teams?" JC asked.

"You two will be teamed up while you're here to work on cases as they come in. The teams that catch the cases do the initial investigation and interviews and based on public interest we'll see if we need to send teams out to arrest or close cases depending on leads that show up."

"What's with the pool table?" I asked.

"This part of the park used to house a shooting range and some of the staff used this as a sort of lunchroom and muster room, but now they use the garage in the back and this is considered our new digs. That pool table is supposed to be picked up and shipped to some orphanage uptown. Until that happens, you and the other teams will have to make yourself comfortable around the table," Ahearn said. "I left a folding table and chairs outside for you and some old reports I want you to familiarize yourself with and learn to ape them as much as possible. I don't want mystery writers down here, just reporters—who, what, when, where, and how. Tonight, there is a team who is catching, and you will man headquarters while I attend a meeting at One PP. So, good luck and call me if you need me," Ahearn said as he headed out the side door.

JC and I looked at each other and we both started to smile.

"Are you kidding me?" JC said. "Who, what, when, why, and how? Is that all he wants? I thought they wanted DEDUCTION?"

"I'm getting the impression he doesn't think much of us as detectives, don't you, JC?" I said.

"Wait until he gets a load of Stamos and his talking gun Betsy. Why, he'll probably wet himself listening to him explaining how when his gun talks, skells listen," JC said.

We both started to laugh at the thought of Stamos listening to the orientation we just went through.

"I'm afraid you were right after all, JC, when you said they will probably put us in some basement in the city, never to be heard of again," I said.

"Well, one good thing, though. We seem to be in charge right now so let's get some coffee and start APING these old reports," JC joked.

Six o'clock came quick and we signed out and headed home.

Karen was in the kitchen and Annie was playing with her Teddy at the kitchen table.

"Hi, hon. How was it?" Karen asked while stirring a pot on the stove.

"Okay, I guess. The boss just told us how they do things down there and he had a meeting, and JC and I went over reports to see how they were written and what crimes were happening. You know, that sort of crappola," I said.

"Michael, don't use words like that around Annie. They are like sponges at this age and I want her to be a lady, okay?" Karen scolded.

I grabbed a beer, popped the top, and sat down to watch the news. It was after eleven o'clock when Karen woke me up in the chair.

"Time for bed, Michael," Karen said.

"I guess I fell asleep," I mumbled.

"Gee, what was your first clue. I left your dinner in the oven if you're hungry, but I think you should come to bed now as you look exhausted," Karen said.

"Yeah, bed sounds good to me," I said as I ambled off to the bedroom and fell into bed in my clothes.

The alarm was the next thing I heard at 7:30 a.m. A new day was about to begin.

"Did you call my dad yet for that golf game?" Karen asked.

"No, but I'll call him today from work. Okay?" I said.

"Don't put it off, Michael. I'm worried about him and his macho go-it-alone attitude about his health," Karen said.

"I hear you. Today. I promise," I said.

CHAPTER *28*

THE FOLLOWING WEEK FLEW BY with JC and me getting to know Manhattan South and the surrounding neighborhoods. The paperwork was taking up all our time and left little room for actual investigation. On Wednesday morning I called my father-in-law, Tom McEvady, and set up a golf date with JC and Tom's friend Alec Walker, a retired bar owner.

"I guess we'll play the Black Course at Bethpage State Park because it's the weekend and that course is too tough for even good players, let alone duffers," I said. "What do you say?"

"Great. Yeah, there won't be a big wait to ruin a weekend by playing yourself into a heart attack. See you about seven a.m.," Tom said.

I never did know when he was kidding, as he was always so droll.

JC caught an assault case while I was on the phone and we were heading over to Avenue A and 7th Street to meet a complainant.

"We're on for golf on Saturday at seven a.m. at Bethpage. The Black Course," I said.

"Oh, shit. Do you have a death wish playing that graveyard of dreams. Hell, even the pros want nothing to do with that course," JC said.

"All golf courses will be packed with a four-hour wait and it'll take us all day to complete the round, while the Black has about a twenty-minute wait," I said.

"The twenty minutes is to take the suicides off the greens," JC said.

"I need to find out from my father-in law what health problem he's keeping from his wife. Ann requested it and Karen asked me to help. I need your help because he thinks a lot of you."

"Stop blowing smoke up my ass, Mike. You know Tom plays everything close to the vest and I think he'll say it's none of our business and be pissed all day," JC said.

"Just give me a hand with him, that's all I ask."

"Yeah, yeah, I'll do what I can," JC said.

After taking the UF #61 (crime report), JC drove up to the Con Edison Building on 14th Street to finish up the details and the referrals.

"Why don't we head back to the office and finish the report like real detectives, JC?" I said.

"I like doing my paper work here," JC said.

Just then a radio broadcast hit the air with a ten-thirty (crime in progress) at 320 East Third Street, a bodega, with "shots fired."

Without hesitation, JC put the car in gear and I put the siren on while sticking the flashing light on the roof.

"Make sure you get us there in one piece, JC," I said. "I think we should be on silent running a few blocks away, so we don't catch a bullet."

"Sounds good," JC said.

We came into the one-way street slowly, looking for anyone moving away from the scene. Without a description, suspicion was all we had.

"There's a marked sector car already on the scene," JC said while pointing ahead.

The rear window burst into a hundred pieces as two bullets careened off the headrest and the dashboard.

"Hit the deck. INCOMING!" JC yelled as he sped up into an alley, stopped the car, and slowly opened the driver side door.

Two more bullets bounced off JC's door, ricocheting into the nearby building. "Damn it! It's a freakin' ambush, Mike."

"Manhattan South robbery car to Central! Ten-four (assist patrolman), shots fired Third between First and Second Avenues."

"Ten-four, Manhattan South," Central Dispatch said.

"All units, assist patrolman in the 9th Precinct, between 3rd Street and 2nd Avenue. Use caution, shots fired. Detective unit under fire in unmarked unit." Central directed all units in vicinity.

"Can you see any movement, JC?" I asked.

"No, but I'm just looking through the rearview mirror. Time to get a better look," JC said as he slid out of the front seat into the street and crawled behind a light pole.

"Anything?" I asked.

"I see somebody peering out of that cellar about three buildings up. Where is the cavalry, man? I'm flying blind here," JC whispered.

"Cover me. I'm gonna try for the pole across the street," I said, kicking the passenger door open and making a run for the telephone pole on the other side of the street.

Bang! Bang! It was the sound and the ping of lead hitting metal. The shooter didn't see me and was still shooting at our car. Two more shots came our way and I returned fire at the muzzle flashes I saw and continued up the sidewalk as I could hear sirens in the distance.

"He's on the move, Mike, heading north on 3rd," JC said as he started up 3rd Street.

I watched the shooter duck into a hallway, break the glass on the lobby door, and run inside.

"He's heading into that apartment house, JC. Give the location to Central and tell them we are on scene in plainclothes."

Reaching the building, I climbed the stoop and started opening the door in the hallway. There was blood on the door handle and the floor had a blood trail leading into the rear apartment. Two uniformed men came into the hall and I held my shield up nice and high and pointed to the blood trail. Lining up on both sides of the apartment door one of the cops banged on it with his nightstick.

"Police. Open up," Officer Levin commanded.

Bang! Bang! Bullets crashed through the door and into the wall behind us. We returned fire through the door.

"Stop firing, man! I give up, you lousy pigs. I quit," the shooter said.

Looking through the huge hole in the door we saw the shooter kneeling on the floor with his hands up. The two uniforms ran in and put cuffs on him while I picked up his gun with a handkerchief and put it in my pocket.

Later, in Bellevue hospital, they dug one bullet out of the shooter's hip and it turned out to be my lucky shot in the alley. The duty captain determined the arrest to be mine and the assist to JC and the two uniforms.

All Sergeant Ahearn could do was shake his head and say, "Some men put in twenty years and never fire a shot."

"Just lucky, I guess," JC said while choking back a smile.

CHAPTER 29

THE DEPARTMENT THOUGHT IT WOULD be a good idea if JC and I took a few days off after the shootings, so we gladly jumped at the chance.

"I called Karen's father today and pushed up our golf date. Can you make it tomorrow, JC?" "Yeah, let's get it over with. See you in the morning," JC said.

Bethpage State Park was a beautiful, well-manicured park that had five courses, each with different levels of difficulty. The Black was the toughest with the Red and Blue close behind, and then came the Green and the Yellow. No one needed to be told which was the toughest as the Black only had a twenty-minute wait compared to waiting hours for the others.

After meeting in the parking lot, the four of us walked through the hallway into the clubhouse with our spikes tap dancing across the marble floors. We approached the first tee and JC read the sign aloud.

"'The Black Course is a test of skill and slow players are encouraged to play one of the other courses. This rule will be enforced by the starter.' When they say slow players don't they really mean crappy players like us?" JC commented.

"Speak for yourself." I said. "Just make sure you hit good drives and second shots, and the starter will leave us alone."

We played teams with Karen's father and his friend Alec Walker teaming up against JC and me. We played best ball and it seemed the two old guys were a couple of hustlers. Tom McEvady was great around the greens, and Alec was long and straight all day. JC and me just argued about who was screwing up the game. But we had a lot of laughs at our expense.

"Did you hear the joke about God and St. Peter playing golf?" JC asked. "St. Peter tees off straight down the fairway and God hits his into the woods where a squirrel picks up the ball and drops it on the fairway, and an eagle swoops down, picks it up, and drops it on the green and into the cup. St. Peter turns to God and says, 'Are you gonna play golf or fuck around?'" JC said while wearing a shit faced grin.

"I don't get it," Alec joked.

"Sounds sacrilegious," Tom said, winking in my direction.

"You guys have no sense of humor. None," JC whined.

"I think the real joke today was you two thinking you were golfers," Tom said. "Drinks, I believe, are on you two young whippersnappers."

Alec and Tom began to laugh and shake hands as if they had done it often. Watching the two old-timers walk into the clubhouse, JC and I looked at each other and knew we had been plucked by two sharpies.

While JC and Alec were playing shuffleboard, I asked Tom how he was feeling. "I'm fine, Mike. Why?"

"Frankly, Tom, Ann came to see Karen and me last week and she was very upset. Thought you were hiding something from her," I said.

"Damn. I never could hide anything from that woman," Tom said while making circles with his beer on the table.

"I know it's none of my business, Tom, but I think you should tell Ann," I said.

"I've been trying to find the right moment. It...it seems I have a cancer on my lung and they wanna operate. There are no guarantees and I worry about how Ann will cope," Tom explained.

We sat in silence for a while taking it all in and not knowing what to say.

"I guess I'll tell her tonight, Mike. Please don't tell Karen yet. I'd like to tell Ann first. Okay?" Tom asked.

I nodded and drank my beer in one gulp. "Sorry, Tom," I said.

When I got home that night Karen started grilling me the minute I walked through the door, but I stuck to my word and told her that her father was telling Ann first and then he'll call you. Karen looked stunned by my rebuke and seemed to know instinctively that the news was bad. Very bad. We sat for a long time that night before the call finally came.

"Hi, Dad," was all Karen said. She sat at the kitchen table rolling the phone cord in her hand and staring at the floor. "When will they operate?" Karen asked. "How's Mom, Dad? Okay. Tell her I'll call tomorrow. Love you, Dad."

Karen hung up the phone and continued to sit there. I put my arms around her and she broke down sobbing uncontrollably.

"Those damn cigarettes. That's what caused it," Karen kept repeating through her tears. "I kept telling him to stop, but he wouldn't listen. Why wouldn't he stop?"

"Smoking is addictive and tobacco companies put stuff in there to feed people's need," I said.

Karen fell asleep on the couch from exhaustion and I slept in a chair, close to her. As my father used to say, "These are the times that try men's souls."

The next few days Karen refused to go anywhere for fear she would miss a call from her parents with a news update. We stayed home and did odd jobs around the house that I had been putting off for weeks and now I wanted to do them to keep busy. I kept dreaming that Tom was walking around saying he was "short" all the time, referring to soldiers in Nam whose time there was getting short. Tom, I assume, meant his time on this planet was short. A terrible dream and one I obviously didn't tell Karen I had as she might think it's an omen, or that I was a terrible husband or both. Either way, I lose, so silence is golden.

Finally, Tom called and said he was scheduled for surgery Monday morning at Long Island Jewish and asked for our prayers. Funny, I knew he was a practicing Catholic, but I didn't think he would ask anyone to pray for him. I suppose that's when I realized just how serious this operation was as he always played his cards close to the vest. Karen dragged me into the living room, sat me down with a pair of rosaries, and we began praying for Tom McEvady. This prayer vigil was repeated every day. I figured Karen's prayers might be answered, but as for me, I hoped God would overlook who was asking and look at the person they were for. I always figured God had a sense of humor because he allowed me get out of Viet Nam and become a cop while so many better men than me never made it home. What's the old saying? "Only the good die young." I guess the rest of us live to a ripe old age where our souls turn black with sin like in *The Picture of Dorian Gray*.

I worked the weekend, twelve-hour tours, so I could take off on Monday for the operation. JC also worked the same hours so in case I needed him he would be available. I was lucky to have a partner like JC. We were beginning to catch a lot of cases involving gang activity in Manhattan South and the boss wanted some results. With all that was going on at home with my family, I couldn't get my head in the game.

CHAPTER *30*

SUNDAY AFTERNOON JC CAUGHT A double homicide inside an abandoned factory at 12th and Avenue C. As we approached the doorway of the factory, the ME (medical examiner) handed us plastic boots and gloves.

"I don't want you dragging anything into the crime scene or away from it. It's a mess in there, so be careful where you step," Dr. Kraft said.

The floodlights were shining bright and the floor looked like a river of blood. Hanging from hooks and chains from the ceiling were two bodies. One female, one male. The only way we could tell their gender was the woman had had her breasts cut off and the man had his genitals removed.

"These fuckers are animals, Mike," JC said.

"From the amount of blood, I have determined the victims were still alive when they were carved up," said Dr. Kraft.

We arrived at the hospital at 9:30 and met Karen's mom, Ann, who was in Tom's room.

"They have scheduled Tom for ten this morning and they will be sending someone to wheel him down to the operating room soon," Ann said.

None of us said anything, just nodded acknowledgement.

"Thanks for coming, Mike," Tom said. "Keep an eye on the women today."

I patted his arm and said, "Sure thing, Tom. Don't worry about anything. Just get better."

Two hospital attendants arrived and asked us to leave the room while they transferred Tom to another gurney. They packed his gear under the gurney and pushed him to the elevator. We all followed behind like ducklings following their mother. Pulling up outside the operating room, the two attendants told us to wait and that someone will be out to take the patient in shortly. "Good luck" one of them said. Ann and Karen were holding Tom's hand when two doctors in scrubs and surgical masks came out and pushed Tom through the swinging doors while we stood in the hallway, watching as the doors closed. As we shuffled around in the hall, Tom's doctor, Harvey Klein, came out and told us not to worry, and that there was a waiting room just outside with coffee and donuts. Klein went over to Ann and told her that he had done this procedure hundreds of times and for her to trust in him and his team.

"I do trust you, Doctor, but if you don't mind, I'll say a few prayers just in case."

Klein smiled and held her hand and said, "We can use all the help we can get." He pulled on his surgical mask and headed back through the swinging doors.

It was a long day filled with fear, boredom, and total exhaustion. I drank so much coffee I didn't think I could close my eyes, or even blink them for that matter. Karen and Ann had fallen asleep several times during the day and, finally, after five and a half hours, Dr. Klein came out.

"Tom is in recovery and the operation was a success. I believe I got all the cancer. We sent it to the lab so I'll know more about it later, but for now, the outlook is good."

"Oh, thank God. Can we see him, Doctor?" Ann asked.

"Give him a couple of hours because he's heavily sedated and needs the rest. I think you should go get something to eat and come back in a little while and by then he will be ready for company. Just a couple at a time though, okay?" Klein said.

We all felt a great relief at the news and I was actually really hungry.

"There's a diner close by so why don't we all go and grab a bite. We need the energy and it will do us good to get a change of scenery," I said.

"Yes, Mom, let's get something to eat and try to relax. I know this has been a terrible ordeal for all of us, and especially you. What do you say?" Karen asked.

Ann agreed and we all breathed a sigh of relief.

Driving to the diner I remembered what my father used to say about people hating hospitals and funeral homes—it reminds us all that someday this will be us or a loved one in this same situation. Right now, I was glad it wasn't me in that operating room, but I knew my time was coming. Like that couple that we found yesterday hanging from those chains. I'll bet they never figured yesterday was the last day of their lives. No, you never know.

It took a couple of days for Tom to get his strength back, but he looked great and the doctor was confident of a full recovery. Karen drove her mom to the hospital every day for a week until he was discharged. JC did some babysitting for me while I did the shopping and household chores.

"Well, Mr. Mom, what's for supper?" JC asked.

"Tonight, I'm making...reservations," I said. "Tom gets home this week and I'll have to help Ann set up the house to accommodate him while he recovers. You know, like bring his bed downstairs, help Karen prepare some meals they can heat and eat, do the shopping they need."

"I know this is family and everything, but Sergeant Ahearn wants to know where we are with that double homicide and I think he's getting tired of listening to me tell him I'm running down leads," JC said.

"After tomorrow I'll tell Karen I need to get crackin' at work, so she'll have to pick up the slack, Okay? Where are we on those leads?" I asked.

"There's some bodega owner named Felix Batista on Avenue C and 3rd Street who says he might have information for us. I thought we could interview him tomorrow. What do you say?" JC asked.

"Okay, set it up for tomorrow," I said.

After taking care of Tom and his needs I left Karen and headed into the office. JC had made an appointment with Batista for noon in interview room three near Ahearn's office, so he could see us actually doing police work. Batista was a nervous, obese little man with a jagged scar down the side of his face.

"Is there a reward for information about those two dead people in the factory?" Batista asked.

"That depends on how good your info is," JC said.

"Why don't you just tell us what you know," I said.

The story was long and winded with what seemed like inconsistencies, especially about how he knew so much.

"So, the woman was in my store earlier in the day to buy cigarettes and beer. There was a Spanish guy waiting for her outside. She was high, man. She almost fell down leaving. The guy held her up while he tried to talk to her. That's when the Robles brothers pulled up and snatched them right off the street," Batista said.

"Nobody saw nothing? A daylight abduction and no complaint made?" JC asked.

"The Robles are killers, man, and I'm gonna need money and the Witness Protection Program," Batista said.

"I guess it's time to call the district attorney, JC. Money and protection is in their purview," I said.

JC called the DA's office and was told to bring Batista right into the office. It seems the Robles brothers had been on their radar for months and the FBI was working with the major case squad compiling a case and this was the breakthrough they were looking for. Assistant District Attorney Landry met us at the door to 50 Centre Street and whisked Batista right into a side office and closed the door in our face.

"What the fuck!" JC mumbled. "What are we chopped liver?"

"Looks like our homicide case takes second fiddle to the Feds," I said.

After a few minutes O'Brien, the DNS investigator, came out and told us we did a great job finding Batista and they wanted us to team up with them for the arrest.

"That was quick. Does that arrest warrant include the double homicide we're working on?" I asked.

"It does. The man and woman they killed were federal informants in the Witness Protection Program. Their names were John and Andrea Castellano," O'Brien said.

"Witness protection? Sounds like somebody screwed up," JC said.

"I'm afraid it wasn't totally our fault this time. The Castellanos tried to blackmail the Robles family but that didn't work out for them. They were free to come and go as they wanted and they made a bad decision," O'Brien said.

"How come nobody notified us?" JC asked. "We didn't even know their name until you told us."

"Batista knew who they were, and when we told him about the Witness Protection Program, he began chirping like a jay bird. I guess this is his way out of the ghetto," OBrien said.

We were brought up to speed by O'Brien and Special Agent Nick Fonseca and we prepared for the assault on the Robles' home turf.

"They own an apartment house on East 3rd Street between 1st and 2nd Avenue. Steel doors and gated windows throughout the building. There are anywhere between ten and one hundred people in there. Jose Robles is a Vietnam vet and the rumor is they have heavy-duty firepower behind those doors. Bring your own weapons, but we will be armed with M-16 and AK-47s along with concussion grenades and tear gas," OBrien rattled off.

"Sounds like it will be a loud party," JC joked.

"Let's hope the surprise is on them," O'Brien said.

CHAPTER *31*

WHILE JC AND I WERE checking our gear, the front doors flew open and in walked Inspector Otto Krueger, followed by what looked like the Green Bay Packers front line.

"Gentlemen, I'm Inspector Krueger and today we are going to take down some low-life murderers who have nothing to lose, so this might be a kill or be killed situation. If there are any here who have reservations about this mission, I would like you to tell me now and I'll replace you without recriminations," Krueger said. Looking around the room, Krueger nodded and said, "We are a go."

Looking over the building diagram, the inspector split up the manpower into six teams with a sergeant in charge and a like number and quantity of weapons for each team. Krueger went over each team's assignment and responsibility several times and stressed watching each other's back. Later I found out he was a light colonel in the Green Berets and the men he brought with him had all served under him while in the service.

We pulled up to the rear of the building without lights and went down into the basement. Someone had already unlocked the door. Team one went to the electrical circuit box and waited for the signal. Two teams were poised at the bottom of the stairs while two teams unlocked the roof door and got into position on the top level. JC and I were positioned at the front of the building to keep people from entering or leaving. No radios were used in the beginning as the static noise could be heard all over the building. Flashlight signals were used instead. Two flashes signaled the basement team to turn off the main circuit breaker. One man stayed near the fuse box and the rest held the elevator in the basement.

"What the hell is going on? Is there a brownout again?"

"Go down to the basement and check the main line, Eddie," Jose Robles said. "Take your weapon."

Eddie Gonzalez trotted down the stairwell with a small flashlight and a 9mm handgun. Reaching the floor landing, Gonzalez was grabbed from behind by one of the Packers and immediately put in a deep sleep. The teams began to ascend the stairs from the bottom while the roof teams came down the stairs from above and on the fire escapes.

"You see anything, Eddie?" Robles yelled. "Something's wrong. Get your guns, men."

Tear gas began exploding on all floors, and concussion grenades thrown through the fire escape windows created the panic the Feds had hoped for. Robles men ran into the hallways and into the waiting arms of Krueger's men.

"Police! Don't move. You're under arrest."

The words barely faded away when the shooting started. The noise of the close-quarter gunshots was deafening and scary as hell. JC and I had moved up into the firefight on the lower landing and had fired at flames from guns fired in our direction. The shootout lasted only thirty seconds, but it seemed an eternity.

"Put the lights back on, men," Krueger ordered. "Is anybody hit?"

The raid went off without a mishap. None of us got touched. There were thirteen of Robles' men dead or wounded, and Jose Robles and his brother Juan died in the exchange that day. With the Robles brothers dead the gang survivors couldn't wait to talk to knock some years off their sentences.

We were up past noon the following day, what with the paperwork and collection of evidence and the property vouchers and impounding of guns, money, and vehicles belonging to the gang members. I thought that once we did all the unusuals and 61s we would be off the hook for a while, but unlike movie cops, this was only the beginning of the case, not the end. We spent several months dealing with the numerous trials that each perpetrator demanded, and sometimes we were assigned to the DA's office for weeks at a time. The boredom of sitting around the courthouse all day waiting to be called to testify was mind numbing.

"How the hell do you lawyers do this day in day out?" I asked.

"Weeks go into preparing for court, and all the statements and alibis have to be verified and cross referenced," ADA Adelson said. "Who can be bored with all this work we do." Adelson smiled.

"Yeah, like what?" JC asked.

Reaching into his desk drawer, Adelson pulled out a piece of paper. "Here, look this over."

I began reading the names of occupations. Teacher, doctor, lawyer, professor. The heading on the page read, "Don't impanel for cause."

"Those are the occupations we try to avoid putting on a jury because they are too analytical when deciding on the guilt or innocence of the defendant. They overthink everything and they need a smoking gun to convict," Adelson said. "Defense attorneys have a list similar to this with occupations like cop, fireman, steel worker, or any blue-collar worker, because they size up individuals quicker than the analytical ones do and are quick to find them guilty. That's the tendency anyway."

"I guess the ideal jury for you would be all blue-collar workers. Right, counselor?" JC said.

"That's why every juror fills out a Voir Dire so we can get an idea who they are and if they are the right fit for us. Obviously, if he's the right fit for me, the defense will object. That's why it takes so long to impanel a jury," Adelson said.

Adelson was a good guy as lawyers go and even JC liked him, but JC was always giving Adelson the needle. "When you went to law school, didn't you guys attend a class that told you that lawyers run the world and that you were godlike?"

Adelson shook his head and smiled but continued to write his closing argument for the morning.

"I guess that's a yes, eh, Mike?" JC quipped.

"The reason I don't act like God's chosen person is because my father was a cop and he said if I ever started to put on airs, he would come back and haunt me to death. My father was a man of his word, so what you see is what you get," Adelson said. "Does that answer your question?"

JC and I just sat there with our mouths open.

"I hope you two don't look like that tomorrow in the witness chair."

We all had a good laugh over that.

"You can't judge a book by its cover, huh, JC?" I said.

"You're alright, Adelson, even if you are a lawyer," JC said.

The trials took over seven months to complete, and five pleaded guilty while seven were convicted after trials. The sentences were from five to fifteen for the plea deals and thirty to life for those who went to trial. Adelson was praised by the DA and mayor and being a smart guy, we knew he was going places. Attorney General Mark Adelson had a good ring to it.

CHAPTER *32*

JC AND I WERE BACK on routine shift duty for only a couple of weeks after the Robles gang trials when we caught a DOA in the men's shelter on East 3rd Street. Officers Sandowsky and Kratzer had the sector and had responded to the job.

"What do we have, Officer?" JC asked.

"We got the call at 1930 hours from the night manager, a Mr. Bob Santangelo. It seems he found Mr. Roy Rogers lying face down in his own blood. Looks like he was stabbed," Kratzer said.

"Roy Rogers?" I said as I bent down for a closer look.

"Yeah, Roy Rogers" Sandowsky laughed. "It has to be an alias, right?"

"No. That's the poor bastard's name all right," I said. "I locked up a couple of muggers who prey on old vets on check day and he was the victim."

"Did you guys touch anything or move the body?" JC asked.

"We didn't, but Santangelo said he rolled him over to try to help him." Kratzer said.

"Any notifications made?" JC asked.

"The sergeant on patrol was notified along with the ME's office. The ambulance attendant from Bellevue, Lyle James, pronounced Mr. Rogers dead at 1850 hours," Kratzer continued.

"I'll call the crime scene unit and put another call into the ME's office," I said.

JC gave me a strange look and pulled me aside. "What's the rush on this guy? He's just another Bowery bum that probably got stabbed over a bottle of cheap booze or a cheese sandwich," JC whispered.

"That poor derelict in there not only fought a war for America, but he was also the witness who saw the guy arguing with Anselmo the night he was killed. He also identified the car he was driving, so to me he was not a worthless individual. Who knows...the case might be connected," I said.

"Sounds like a long night," JC said.

Back in the office we filed all the paperwork in the open case basket, including the 61s, aided cards, witness statements, and evidence and property vouchers, and we even typed up an unusual for the borough commander.

"I guess that's about all. Right, Mike?" JC asked.

"All except for the elephant in the room," I said.

"What are you carrying on about now, Mike?" JC asked.

"All this time we assumed that Roy Rogers had seen Oliveri arguing with Anselmo that night across from the men's shelter, but what if we're wrong. What if it was someone else?" I said.

"You mean, like the boss man?" JC said.

"Yeah, like the boss man," I said.

"You might be right, but maybe we should hand this over to IAD and let them run with it," JC said.

We both sat at our desks for a while before I stood up and said, "You're right. IAD has the time and the resources to look into this case and I think the sooner we notify them the better for all concerned."

We left a message for IAD that we had information concerning a case-involved officer shooting and that we would be down the next day for an interview and to present the evidence, what little there was.

"I'll put us on the day tour roll call tomorrow for court. I'll let the boss know face to face tomorrow. Right now, I gotta call Karen and tell her I'm staying at the station house tonight, but I'll be home tomorrow evening."

I watched JC go into the boss's office and make a call. I figured it was to one of his bimbos.

"Are you sleeping here tonight?" I asked.

"Maybe, later. Right now, I have to meet someone. See you later, Mike," JC said.

I watched him leave through the sergeant's locker room and wondered what secret JC was keeping. Whatever it was I figured I'd find out sooner or later. Tonight, though, I just fell into the closest bed by the door and began snoring.

JC woke me at 0700 hours. He was showered and dressed already and had bought coffee and buttered rolls for us.

"Wow! What got your motor revving this morning?" I joked.

"Just good genes, I guess. I never needed much sleep. Besides, we have a lot to do this morning," JC said.

Before we left for Schermerhorn Street, I told Sergeant Ahearn where we were going, but I left out some vital details, like we were investigating a cop for a cop's murder. I thought the less said the better.

"Did you tell Ahearn why we were going to IAD?" JC asked.

"I kept the reason secret for now. Loose lips sink ships," I said.

"Yeah, the walls have ears in this department," JC said.

The Internal Affairs Office was at the end of Schermerhorn Street in an old, seedy part of Brooklyn. The street was surrounded by old factory buildings and auto body shops. All things considered, a perfect place for what the cops called the "rat" squad.

Lieutenant Royce's office was on the second floor at the end of the narrow hallway. The glass door only said "Investigations." We opened the door and seated behind the only desk in the room was a ferret-like, little bald man with dark-rimmed glasses and a pearl-handled Colt revolver in a shoulder holster.

Walking over to his desk, I held out my hand and said, "I'm Detective Mike Halley and this is my partner, John Colby."

Royce shook my hand and nodded to JC and sat down. "Now, I understand you have information on a cop shooting? What cop?"

We spoke for over an hour and gave him all we had, and we added our own suspicions, which he seemed to dismiss out of hand.

On the way out, the door Royce assured us of a full and determined investigation. We asked him to keep us in the loop if he could. Royce nodded again, and I began to take the nodding as a "don't hold your breath" sign. No matter. If they catch Oliveri's boss, all this secret BS will be worth it. On the way back to Manhattan, JC and I never spoke a word until we drove onto Delancey Street from the Brooklyn Bridge.

"You think that ferret-face fuck is any good?" JC asked.

"Well, one thing he has going is he sure don't look like a cop," I said. "Oliveri's boss would never make him."

"Let's hope he's smarter than he looks, because I wasn't impressed either by Royce or that shithole office they work out of," JC complained.

"Yeah, I'm afraid I agree with you. Let's hope we're wrong," I said.

CHAPTER 33

THE WEATHER WAS COLD IN New York and Karen was staying at her mother's for the next week or so, at least until her father could move around a bit. It had been some time since I was alone, and I was getting antsy hanging around. I ran into an old friend from the 9th Precinct and he invited me to a poker game on the Island—Deer Park to be exact—and I asked if I could bring JC and they said I should bring all the "suckers" you want. JC wasn't thrilled when he heard it was John Merryweather and Billy Moyes.

"Are those two phonies still outside of prison?" JC joked. "What the hell do you see in those two? You can't believe a word they say."

"How do you know they lie?" I asked.

"Because their mouths are moving, that's why," JC said.

"Just try to see if you can keep from getting knocked on your ass and have a few laughs for a change," I joked.

"I guess I'll never live down Balboni, right?" JC said. "Especially with you around to remind me, hump."

We pulled into Moyes's driveway and parked behind his car.

"Look, he drives a cop car," JC said while pointing to a dark Ford sedan with black rimmed tires and a big spotlight on the driver's side window. "You think he wears his badge on his pajamas?"

"I thought you were gonna be nice tonight," I said.

We knocked on his front door and rang the bell, but there was no response. After some yelling at his windows, we went around to the back of the house and there he was. Moyes was sitting on top of his roof holding onto the chimney.

"Thank God you guys came. I was ready to try jumping down to the ground," Moyes said.

"What happened? Did the ladder fall down?" I asked.

"No. My wife didn't want me going out tonight, so she took the ladder away and left me here."

"Oh, yeah. This just keeps getting better and better, Mike," JC said while we put the ladder upright against the house.

"Man, you could have frozen to death up there. That's a good, clean way to kill off a husband," JC said.

"Well, are we still on for the night or what?" I asked.

"Damn right, we are. Come on, let's get going to Mayweather's so I can take your money," Moyes said.

I waited for JC to start ribbing Moyes, but he just looked at him with a strange expression all night as if he were lost in deep thought.

It was well after four o'clock when the game finally ended. JC was the big winner and I won a few, but Mayweather and Moyes were big losers.

"I'll need to stop at an ATM on the way home," Mayweather said. "My wife thinks I always win playing poker. That's why she puts up with it."

JC looked at him but never said a word.

After we dropped Moyes and Mayweather off and I was headed back to my house to get JC's car, I asked him. "What's with you?"

"What?" JC asked.

"You never said a word all night about those two. Cat got your tongue?" I asked.

"Look, Mike, I've been seeing this girl Maggie for a while now and I was wondering if marriage was right for me or not. Watching Moyes get left on the roof by his wife and the deception that Mayweather practiced has me real confused. What's your take?" JC said.

"Well, I'm glad you found someone. Does she go to the Helen Keller school for the blind?" I laughed.

"Very funny, hump. I'm serious about this. Are all marriages based on lies, deception, and control?" I could see that JC was serious and I don't know why but it unnerved me.

"If you're serious about this girl, my advice is to use those two guys you saw tonight as the worst examples of husbands you could find. Do the exact opposite of what you saw and you might make it as a good husband," I said.

"Like how, Mike?" JC asked.

"I find that people who lie in a marriage usually lie all through their life, and sooner or later the lies catch up with you. Marriage is supposed to be a partnership, without secrets. Lies perpetuate secrets and if you get caught lying, you've lost trust, and after trust love will surely follow," I said.

"What about all the shit I pulled. Do I tell her about my past?" JC asked.

"Only if your past will interfere with your future as a couple. Sometimes the past should be buried, and you should concentrate on the future. You have to grow up when you get married and not think you can do all bachelor nonsense, like staying out late with the boys or gambling to a point that hurts your family. Being married carries with it awesome responsibilities. When you put your wife and kids first, you'll have no problem, JC," I said.

The rest of the ride home was as quiet as a wake.

I didn't see JC for the next few weeks as he was in court testifying about an old case he had before we were partners. On paper, I was teamed up with Bob Stamos, but I ended up manning the squad phones while Stamos and me caught up to our mountain of paperwork.

"I can't believe I let all these reports go unfinished," Stamos said.

"Yeah, did you know that the borough commander wants to be notified about any case that might be newsworthy. Hell, every case could be newsworthy," I said.

"Might as well send them an unusual for all cases that come across our desk. That way we'll be sure to follow the guideline," Stamos added.

Looking off into space, Stamos pondered the question. How many trees have to die just to keep people in the loop about crime in the city? Stamos shook his head and started typing again.

"Did you see all those signs about the retirement dance/dinner?" Stamos asked.

"Yeah, sure. Are you going?" I asked. "You bet. The Waldorf Astoria throws a good party. My wife loves it," Stamos said.

"Is that crazy partner of yours going?" Stamos asked.

I just shrugged my shoulders in the negative and wondered to myself if JC was going and if he were taking Maggie, his little secret. For all his hatred for secrets, JC held onto this one tight. It had been weeks since he started dating her and I still hadn't been introduced. "I'll ask him when he gets back from court," I said.

To my surprise JC said he was going to the dinner and Maggie would be along for the ride.

"That's great," I said. "Karen will have someone to talk to. These dinners can be a mind-numbing experience."

"You love it. Hobnobbing with the brass and rubbing shoulders with real cops," JC joked.

"I would just watch out for the mai tais this year. You lost the ability to walk last year." I started to laugh.

"Screw you, hump. Somebody spiked the punch last year." JC smiled. "I'll see you tonight."

CHAPTER 34

THE NIGHT OF THE RACKET was chilly but was well attended. The mayor and his assorted sycophants were all in attendance, along with all the brass from chief of the department, chief of detectives, and numerous precinct commanders. The dais was filled with old-time detectives who had done the job without two-way radios, computers, or even cameras, and had broken the cases from the Brinks Robbery to the FBI murders in Brooklyn. These guys were right out of central casting. They looked like cops with the broken noses, rumpled suits, and protruding beer bellies, to round out the picture. There wasn't a college graduate among them, but when it came to doing the job, these were the templates for those who would follow. They had fought a world war and a police action in Korea, learned to stretch a pot of soup into dinner for six people, and raised large families who would bring with them the work ethic of their parents. Yes, these were the men I had aspired to be but had fallen woefully short of. Anselmo would have been on the dais this night because he fit with these good men, and had it not been for a murdering cop, he would have been honored tonight.

Walking over to our table was JC and a good-looking blonde he introduced me to as "his little secret. This is Maggie, Mike."

"Hello, Maggie. Nice to finally meet you. This is my wife, Karen."

After all the introductions were completed, we all sat down for dinner and a few speeches. I had to hand it to the mayor for his nerve. During his administration he had police corruption, the Knapp Commission, and a police strike, so being at a police racket was the last place he wanted to be. Hell, some of these men on the dais were investigated by His Honor and his Internal Affairs lackeys. Funny how

167

all the investigations stopped as soon as they began looking into judges. Hypocrisy knows no boundaries.

During dinner Karen had struck up a conversation with Lorraine Ahearn, Sergeant Ahearn's wife. A personable, but timid woman, she seemed content to be in Ahearn's shadow, a position Karen abhorred. The conversation was lighthearted about family and friends, and then a name came up, almost matter-of-factly—Oliveri. She said, "I never met too many of John's friends, but Oliveri was one I didn't like. He made me nervous," Lorraine said.

"You met Oliveri?" I asked.

"Yes. Isn't that awful. The only friend of John's I ever met and he was a bad person."

"They were friends, John and Oliveri?" I asked.

"Didn't you know that? They were in the academy together, I think," Lorraine said.

The rest of the conversation just trailed off as I was mulling over what I had just heard. Oliveri and Ahearn. Friends. Academy together. Is this why Ahearn requested JC and me after our promotion? To keep an eye on us? I grabbed JC and told him of the revelations and said to meet me for breakfast in the morning at our house, so we could talk. JC nodded in a fog-like state.

The following morning JC was at my front door at 7:00 a.m. with Dunkin' Donuts under his arm.

"I'll need some coffee to go with the donuts," JC said.

I poured two cups of coffee and we both sat down without another word. I took a sip of coffee and decided it needed more sweetener.

"Thanks for the donuts. I was starving," I said.

JC got up and brought the coffee carafe to the table, poured two more cups of coffee, and grabbed another donut.

"Well, what now?" JC asked.

"You know as much as I do, so what do you think our next move is?" I asked.

"Maybe we should just put a bullet in Ahearn and be done with it," JC said.

"Murderers we're not. What about IAD? Information like this could get the case moving," I said.

"I can't believe the son of a bitch is our boss and he's been watching every move we made since Anselmo's murder," JC said.

"I guess the best bet for us is to notify Lieutenant Royce in IAD and see how he wants us to play it," I said.

"We're going into work this morning knowing about this guy?" JC whined.

We called Lieutenant Royce and he wanted us in his office forthwith. We were the only cops in his office that early in the morning and he had two other investigators standing by. We told him what we had, and he called for a warrant on Ahearn's phone and home.

"I hope there's enough here to make a case against the sergeant, but if there isn't, your time in this borough is over with any way you look at it," Royce said. "I think you will be assigned to IAD until this case is resolved one way or the other."

JC scrunched up his face as he always did when he wanted to say something but was afraid to.

"What? What is it?" I asked.

"Is that it for us on this case?" JC asked. "We go out with a phone call?"

We both looked at Royce as he shrugged his shoulders and sat down awaiting the results of the search warrant. It was well over two hours before we heard anything back about the warrant. Royce answered the phone on its first ring.

"IAD. Lieutenant Royce speaking," Royce said. He sat there listening intently, rolling the wire around his fingers. "Fine. Let me know any updates," Royce said.

JC and I were both coming out of our seats waiting for word.

"Well, what happened?" JC blurted out.

"Good news, bad news," Royce said. "The good news is they found the proceeds of some diamond heists done in the borough, along with many phone calls to Oliveri on subsequent nights of the stickups and burglaries. That is on the plus side, but the bad news is there is no sign of Ahearn. His wife said he emptied their safe this morning and left.".

"Left? He's into the wind, man," JC complained. "Where the hell can a wanted cop go?"

"His wife said there was a lot of cash and some jewelry as well. A shock to her as well as us," Royce said. "We put out an APB on him, and all airlines and ship lines have been notified, along with Interpol. He won't get far. It's only a matter of time before Ahearn is brought to justice for the murder of a police officer. You men did your job, now let us do ours. You two go home and take a couple of days off and I'll notify the borough commander about what's going on and that you will be assigned to IAD until further orders." Royce slapped JC on the back. "Good work, men."

Leaving IAD in Brooklyn left an empty feeling inside me and I told JC as much.

"You think I like leaving the rat bastard running loose like that?" JC said. "We should've capped the bastard."

"Ahearn was an organizer, so he would have a contingency planned for just such an event. He's probably on some beach in a country without an extradition treaty with us. At least he'll have his way until the money runs out."

"I can't believe he left his wife like that to face her ruined life alone. That was cold, man," JC said. "Listen, I'm going to stop off at the Inn for a couple of brewskis, so can I interest you in a few?" JC asked.

"I need to tell Karen about what happened to her friend Lorraine Ahearn today. She needs to hear it from me rather than hear it on the news. I'll call you later tonight, JC," I said as I left the car and headed up the driveway.

I opened the front door and threw my keys on the desk. "Karen. You home?"

"Yeah, Karen is home, Detective," Ahearn said, as he held his gun to Karen's head.

CHAPTER 35

"HAVE YOU LOST YOUR MIND, Ahearn? The world is looking for you. There is no escape," I said.

"Escape? Escape? Ha ha! There is no escape for me or for you now that you shoved your nose in my business," Ahearn said.

"You want a hostage, take me, not Karen," I said.

"You come over to the chair and sit down," Ahearn said, motioning to the chair with his gun.

Sitting on the La-Z-Boy, Ahearn pushed the chair into the incline position and began tying me up. Pulling my service revolver from its holster, he threw it on the stove in the kitchen.

"I figure to wait it out for a while until things cool down and I can move again. Who the hell would think I'd be at the cop's house who tripped me up?" Ahearn said.

"Look, let Karen go and I'll do whatever it takes for your freedom," I said.

"Oh, don't worry. You'll do whatever I need to get free or your little family will end tonight. Since my life is over I don't see why I shouldn't end yours, too," Ahearn said.

Looking around the living room, Ahearn went to the photo on the TV and said, "Where is the child?"

"Annie is at my mother's for the weekend. She won't be home until Sunday evening," Karen said.

"You better be telling me the truth because anything out of the ordinary I start shooting. With nothing to lose, reason is lost on me. Do you understand, Halley? Nothing...to...lose!" Ahearn repeated.

"I get it. Don't lose your head. You can still make it out of here, so stay calm," I said.

"Don't you worry about me staying calm. Calm is my middle name. You just do what I tell you and maybe, just maybe, you'll live to tell your grandkids what happened. Or maybe I'll eliminate your family and end this nonsense once and for all. So, just do what I tell you or...else," Ahearn said, waving his gun in my direction. "Or else."

The sun began to shine through the blinds in the living room as I tried to move my hands and feet, which were numb from being in one position all night long. Karen had fallen asleep in her chair while handcuffed to the couch. Ahearn was seated on a bar stool in the corner of the room peering out through the curtains.

"How about a bathroom break, Ahearn?" I asked.

"We'll see," Aheam said. "Your wife can go first, then put on my coffee and something to eat. Then, I'll send you."

Ahearn took the cuff off Karen's wrist and allowed her to go to the bathroom after looking over the room and noticing there was no window.

"Keep the door open, Mrs. Halley. There are no secrets in this house," Ahearn said while smiling that phony plastic smile I had come to recognize hid the more sinister intent of the man. "Here's how we're gonna play this scenario. After your wife is done in the bathroom she will start breakfast, and while she's doing that I will let you into the bathroom knowing full well I am out here with a gun pointed at her head. Having your wife as a hostage makes it easier for me to control you, but my backup plan is to kill the both of you and wait until tonight to try to make it out of the city. So, with my backup plan in mind, I think you should play nice, eh, Halley?" Ahearn said.

Nodding in agreement, I pointed to the bathroom and said, "My turn?" The plastic cuffs on my wrists and feet left large red welts where the blood had pooled. Ahern cut the cuffs off.

"Keep the door open and don't take all day," Ahearm instructed.

I looked all over the bathroom for a knife or scissors, anything I could use as a weapon. I felt Ahearn was desperate and he really had nothing to lose by killing us and leaving tonight. Ahearn had looked over the bathroom pretty well and removed anything I could use as a weapon. He must have done it during the night. While Karen was in the kitchen cooking bacon the phone began to ring.

"It might be the job," I said. "They said they would call today with instructions."

"Instructions? Instructions?" Ahearn said as he moved toward me in a menacing stance, but he composed himself and stiffened up.

"These are your instructions for today. The next time the phone rings you answer it with short yes or no answers, no cute sayings or attempts at signaling or codes, because I will start killing you, Halleys, immediately. Do you understand?" Ahearn, said.

Karen and I both nodded that we understood. I could see how desperate he was, and I was beginning to feel just as desperate as Ahearn. I couldn't let this sociopath come in here and kill my whole family without doing something about it. My mind was racing. Who might call today? Royce? JC? What could I say that would alert them? Would Ahearn kill us if cops surrounded our house? The phone began ringing. It startled me. I looked at Ahearn and he picked it up and put it to my ear.

"Hello," I said.

"Good morning, Detective Halley. This is Lieutenant Royce and I wanted to tell you we haven't heard anything new about the case."

"So, JC and me will go into the borough command like you said yesterday. We'll go tomorrow, Lieutenant," I said.

"Yes. Yeah, the borough. All notifications have been made so I'll see you tomorrow," Royce said.

"Goodbye, Lieutenant," I said.

"All right, now let's eat something, so I can tie you up again and wait until tonight to get out of here," Ahearn said.

A crazy thought ran through my mind. Rush him and go for the gun while you have the ability to move before he ties us up for the day. Just then the phone began ringing again.

"Who the hell is that?" Ahearn said, picking up the phone and putting it to my ear.

"Hey, hump. It's JC. Royce just called and told me we were gonna be at the borough tomorrow, so I guess I'll see you then."

Was JC just telling me he got a call from Royce or did they get my message? I could only hope.

We sat at the kitchen table with my wrist cuffed to the stove and sipped coffee and ate bacon while I contemplated my next move.

"How the hell did you ever hook up with Oliveri?" I asked.

Smiling broadly, Ahearn looked at me and said, "We were kindred spirits. I watched him beat a man to death one day and I got him out of trouble. Since that day, I was the brain behind all that brawn. I was shocked when they told me you killed Oliveri" Ahearn said.

"Truth be told, JC killed Oliveri, not me," I said. "Oliveri had me cold in that alley."

"I should have looked in on JC first then, I suppose. But no harm, no foul. There's still time, right, Halley? Ha ha," Ahearn said.

Standing up, Ahearn grabbed Karen by the arm and put her in a chair and cuffed her to the sofa. Walking over to the window, Ahearn pulled back part of the curtain and pried open the blind slat to look out into the driveway.

"What the fuck?" he said.

There was the sound of glass breaking as Ahearn staggered backward over the kitchen table and onto the floor. I tried to get to the gun he dropped but I couldn't get the stove and the cuffs to cooperate.

"Are you all right, Karen?" I asked.

"Yes. What just happened?" Karen yelled.

The front door flew open and emergency service cops poured in from the front and back.

"Is everyone okay, Officer?" Lieutenant Royce said.

"We are now. That was a nice shot. I don't think Ahearn knew what hit him," I said.

After freeing myself from the cuffs, I went over to see how Karen was doing. She was shaking and crying softly.

"Oh, my God, Michael. We could have been killed. Thank God Annie wasn't here with this monster. How did they know he was here?" Karen asked.

"Royce knew we were assigned to IAD, not going back to the borough to work. That gave him the heads up something was wrong at the Halley house," I said.

The rest of the night was a blur with all the brass converging on the scene, and handshaking and pats on the back for catching a cop killer. JC was in his element, retelling the story over and over how we stumbled over the picture of Oliveri and Ahearn and the phone calls that transpired between them.

"Remember when I said Second Grade here we come? Well, here we come, Mike," said JC.

JC was happy, the brass was happy, and the city could live in peace once more, or at least that's what the mayor said at his long-winded speech, along with all the political goodwill he could get out of what happened. The only unhappy people tonight were Ahearn's parents who would try to come to terms with the fact they raised a monster for a child.

I kept thinking to myself that there was some justice in the world in that Mike Anselmo's murder was solved and I had a hand in bringing that about, but I was only fooling myself. Tomorrow there will be other cases, other murders that will demand justice. I wondered how long JC and I would continue on this merry-go-round of life before we burned out?

JC put it succinctly when he said, "Some days we're the dog, and some days we're the fire hydrant."

Today was the day of the dog.

THE END

92902589R00102

Made in the USA
Middletown, DE
11 October 2018